D1389935

BUILD YOUR OWN
FARM BUILDINGS

An example of what can be done by farm labour – an attractive modern-style farmworker's house built on a Cambridgeshire farm.

BUILD YOUR OWN FARM BUILDINGS

By
FRANK HENDERSON

DAIRY FARMER (BOOKS) LIMITED
LLOYDS CHAMBERS, IPSWICH
1955

First Edition
October 1955

PRINTED BY W. S. COWELL LTD
AT THE BUTTER MARKET, IPSWICH

CONTENTS

ILLUSTRATIONS

9

At 113 starts a 32-page section of useful farm building blueprints. Those reproduced on pages 118, 119, 120, 121, 124, 126, 127, 134, 136, 137, 142 and 143 are
acknowledged to the Ministry of Agriculture, Fisheries and Food 'Fixed
Equipment on the Farm' leaflets, and to 'Post-war Building Studies' No. 17;
they are reproduced by permission of the Controller of H.M. Stationery Office.

ILLUSTRATIONS

*Illustrations marked * in this list are acknowledged gratefully to the Cement and Concrete Association; those marked † to the Electrical Development Association; the picture facing page 41 to the Timber Development Association.*

11

FOREWORD

By Earl De La Warr, P.C.

FRANK HENDERSON has many qualifications for writing just such a book as this. Above all, he is a successful small farmer who has succeeded by his own energy and resource rather than by access to large sums of capital.

Great Britain is essentially a country of small farms, most of which need drastic replanning and equipment. This applies especially to their buildings. I am doubly convinced of this since a recent visit to the United States. The impression that I gained there was that America has less to teach us in mechanization on the land than in the saving of labour and effort in the farmyard and buildings. This is a matter partly of equipment but also of planning and layout.

On the other hand, the tendency of the prices that farmers receive, and their ever-rising costs, are such that they must be careful not to burden themselves with excessive capital charges for expensive schemes of improvement.

A treatise such as this should, therefore, be of great value to them if it makes them less dependent on an over-busy building industry whose estimates for small farm jobs are too frequently based on not wanting to do them; and on the fairly considerable number of cups of tea which seem to have to be consumed during the normal builders' hours.

Buckhurst Estate,
Withyham,
Sussex.

AUTHOR'S PREFACE

In my life as a farmer I have found the necessity of having adequate buildings. But if they are to be economical under present conditions the cost of erection must not be too great – and the layout must be such that they make for increased production.

This means, in many cases, that the farmer must design and erect them with the labour already on the farm. This I have done on my own farm, and I have often felt the need for a book which would give me both ideas for design and details of actual work.

If one has the time – and money – all the answers can be found in many books; but the farmer wants one volume which will give the answers to his problems, without a lot of technical detail.

I have endeavoured to achieve this in this book, in the sincere hope that it will help fellow farmers to have better buildings at a cost which will enable them to make better profits from their farming.

Oathill Farm,   *October, 1955*
Enstone,
Oxfordshire.

CHAPTER I

MAKE YOUR BUILDINGS
PAY THEIR WAY

THE cost of farm building – in common with the cost of most other farm needs – has risen considerably. Indeed, so expensive has building become that there is today a tendency to advocate managing without farm buildings wherever possible.

The feeling is understandable. But it should not be carried too far. For a wisely planned farm building can be a financial advantage in many ways.

It can reduce costs of production by saving labour.

It can lead to increased output by accommodating more stock.

It can increase production in relation to food consumed.

It can give greater comfort to workers and stock – and so increase production.

It can save wear and tear on machinery.

It can save waste of manure and so increase yields of crops or reduce expenditure on fertilizers.

So, to my mind, the proper approach to farm buildings is not to try and do without them but instead to consider any building idea you have – either for new buildings or for conversions to an old building – from four points of view:

1. Will it pay?
2. Will it fit into future farm developments?
3. How can it be planned for maximum economy in labour and production when in operation?
4. How can it be most economically built?

MAKE MONEY OR SAVE MONEY

On the first point you should take several aspects into consideration. Where you expect to get·*extra* output, work out the *extra* profit a year it should bring you. Where it should *save* labour, work out what the *saving* is likely to be in the course of a year. And try to put a yearly cash value on any other advantages.

Total them all up and you will then have an idea how much capital you can justifiably spend on the building. For example, a building which you reckon will earn or save an extra £350 a year would justify your spending up to £7,000 – for that would be a 5 per cent return on capital.

It will pay to go into these figures carefully; such a lot depends on them. And, if you have to borrow capital, or prefer to borrow it rather than disturb investments, then detailed figures will have the most influence on your bank manager, building society, Agricultural Mortgage Corporation Ltd, or Lands Improvement Company.

INCOME TAX ALLOWANCE

Bear in mind, too, that where income tax is being paid, then – as the law stands at present – an investment allowance of 10 per cent of the total cost can be set against income tax and, each year for the next ten years, a further 10 per cent can be claimed.

Let me make this quite clear. If you spend £1,000 on a building, then, on your tax returns for the year, you can enter as a claim the investment allowance of £100 *plus* the first year's allowance of one-tenth – another £100. You will have a tax remission on this £200. At 9s in the £1 this means a saving of £90. At 19s in the £1 it means a saving of £190.

Each of the subsequent nine years a further £100 can be entered as a claim. Thus the total saving, at 9s in the £1 tax level, is £90 in the first year and £45 for each of the next nine years – £495. At 19s in the £1 tax level the total saving is £190 in the first year and £95 for each of the next nine years – £1,045.

FUTURE FARM DEVELOPMENTS

The second point – whether the building will fit in with future farm developments – also calls for a lot of detailed consideration. Progress in management techniques can quickly render a building out of date if it is unadaptable.

So there should be scope for extension or for complete interior replanning if the need arises.

Point three calls not only for practical thinking but imaginative thinking. The bold use of a sloping site; excavations on level sites to create labour-saving loading ramps; the use of gravity for food movement; principles of self-feeding – all such ideas should be studied if an easy-working, cost-saving system can result.

That, too, is a point I will discuss more fully when we get down to example plans.

The fourth point – building at the lowest possible cost consistent with quality of work – is going to be the main point of this book.

SAVE HALF THE COST

'Build it yourself' is the key. Many farmers and farm workers are quite capable of tackling much of the building work on a farm, especially alterations and additions to existing buildings.

In many cases all they need is encouragement and a basic understanding of the principles involved and of the right techniques to employ with bricks, timber and concrete.

Further, the cost of farm labour employed on building work, charged – as it should be – to the capital account, and not to ordinary farm expenditure, becomes part of the cost of the buildings on which you will make your income tax claims.

That is the way to save capital. Buildings erected by farm labour in slack periods can be put up for half the price that would be charged if the work is put in a builder's hands.

CHAPTER II

PLANNING A NEW
FARM BUILDING

WHEN a new farm building is required it would be nice if a farmer could look through a range of standard plans and pick the one which just fitted all his circumstances and requirements.

Unfortunately that is rarely possible. Nearly every farm requires something different. The size of farm influences the size of buildings; natural site conditions influence both size and shape; the farmer's methods of stock husbandry and his range of interests are determining factors also.

So, to plan a new building or a conversion to an old one usually involves starting almost from scratch.

SEE LATEST IDEAS

But not quite from scratch. Time spent in studying new and improved buildings on other farms – either by personal inspection or from published plans – will be well spent. Ideas incorporated in them can be adapted, and possibly improved.

That, I think, is the first step to take when setting out to plan a new or converted farm building.

See all the latest ideas you can and make use of all those which will fit into the systems of management you prefer and will help you to produce the goods more cheaply.

MAKE BUILDINGS ADAPTABLE

Next, as I have already briefly mentioned, I think it is wise to give a lot of thought to possible future farm developments so that the new or altered building will not only be useful for the purpose for which it was erected but can be readily adapted to another purpose if the need should arise.

It is worth remembering the extent to which many farm buildings still standing (some of them sound enough to stand for many years yet) have outlived husbandry practices.

There are farms with cowsheds which have been superseded by yard-and-parlour systems; there are large barns built for stacking corn in sheaves on farms where combines are now used. Such is the changing pattern of farming practices today.

Looking ahead, in the near future I do not think we shall need dairies as we know them today. In-churn milking, chemical sterilization and bulk collection will alter all that. The latter will mean taking special care in siting the dairy for accessibility by tanker.

The trouble is that we cannot foresee all the new methods which will come along.

IMPORTANCE OF WIDE SPAN

However, I think it is possible to lay down certain guiding principles which can be applied to all main farm buildings and will make them as elastic as bricks, mortar and concrete can be!

The first is that a new main building should have a fairly wide span, not less than 25'. This gives plenty of scope internally. It allows for housing different kinds of stock; it provides for wide enough passages so that tractors can be used for hauling foods in and manure out. That is a most important provision.

Secondly, a new building should, if possible, be of frame construction, and all interior fittings should be independent of the main frame. This allows for rearranging the interior to suit a different method of husbandry or to accommodate a different form of livestock.

The larger the building, the more important it is that conversion should be possible. If a small pig-sty comes to a useful end, the loss is only a few pounds. But if you suddenly give up using a £3,000 cowhouse and find no alternative use for it, then you have a lot of capital idle which ought to be usefully employed on some other form of production.

Another point I have already briefly mentioned with regard to planning a building is the question of siting. For general building a level site is preferred. But for farm buildings a sloping site may

Top picture: way of making use of a sloping site.
Below: planning to save labour on level site.

23

be an advantage. Such a site enables one to make best use of the natural levels for constructing ramps for loading and unloading.

If the site is level, then other means of achieving the same effect should be considered. For example, the road against the building could be run down into a wide trench to bring the floors of lorries and trailers level with the floor of the building.

Careful planning in respect of this can lead to considerable economy in labour in handling the materials and goods that go into and are taken out of the building (often daily, as with churns of milk) over many years.

VALUE OF WIDE ROADWAYS

Another aspect of siting is the relationship between the chosen site, the existing or proposed new road and any other existing buildings.

As road transport tends to get larger, a fair amount of space needs to be left between buildings.

In my opinion the roadway between two buildings should not be less than 15'. This allows for wide loads, and for passing of normal farm transport. It is also some safeguard against fire risk.

Where the land can be spared, 20'-wide roads would be better still from each point of view. They will involve more making up, but the extra work is worth it in the long run. It is a great mistake to have soft ground between buildings – it gets in a mess whatever you do about it.

PLANNING TO SAVE LABOUR

Finally, but of great importance, comes the question of planning a farm building – whether a new one or a conversion – to make the most economical use of labour when in operation.

A building that is badly planned in this respect can lose the farmer the wages for a man in the course of a year. That is an extreme possibility, but I have known such a saving to be made by alterations to many a piggery.

A lot of labour can be saved by proper cowshed planning, too.

For example, if the dairy is put at one end of an 80-cow double-row shed, the cowman will have to walk ten miles a week carrying milk from cows to dairy. Put the dairy in the middle of one side and the walking distance is reduced to 7½ miles – a difference of 130 miles a year, and every mile involves time that has to be paid for but produces nothing.

STUDY WILL BE REPAID

I do want to stress how essential all these matters are and how important it is that they are all properly considered and that the various advantages and disadvantages of the many alternative ways of designing a new building or a conversion are examined and weighed up.

The hours you spend at this stage of the proceedings in trying out, on paper, first one scheme and then another to find the one which will involve the least walking about will be steadily repaid, week by week and year by year, once the building is in use.

Remember, too, that advice on farm buildings is freely available through the NAAS. The service's experts in farm building design and layout are in touch with the latest ideas; they can suggest which ideas can be suitably applied in your case, and they can tell you where they are in operation so that you can go and 'see for yourself'.

The NAAS officers will also draw up rough plans for you, based on what you decide is the best layout for a particular building.

Similar help can be obtained through the Agricultural Land Service by getting in touch with the Land Agent of your county agricultural executive committee.

GETTING PERMISSION TO BUILD

When you have reached the 'rough-plan' stage – whether the roughs are your own or an NAAS officer's – the next step is to find out whether the approval of the town and country planning authority and of the local urban or rural council is necessary.

Please turn to page 28

This farm building layout was devised by the author in 1942. It serves to illustrate the amount of forethought required in planning a group of buildings.

The main aim in this case was to keep cost as reasonable as possible – without sacrificing the comfort of the workers and stock, or the appearance of the buildings.

The main building is under one roof, with roof lights down the whole length of each side of the roof. Additional lighting is provided where necessary; for example, windows in the cowshed wall put light onto the cows' udders.

Round-the-corner sliding doors enable tractor and trailer to go right through for cleaning out the cowshed. The central feeding passage permits easy feeding from the food-store for the cows in the shed; those in loose boxes (except the isolation boxes) are fed from the same passage – through wall hatches.

Staff room can have a heated cupboard, warmed by electricity or hot pipe from the boiler, to dry coats etc.

By having the Dutch barn immediately behind the buildings the movement of hay and straw is reduced to a minimum; roots can be stored in this barn if required.

Having the covered yards next to the Dutch barn again reduces movement of food; and the fact that there is a roadway right round the yards enables yarded stock to be fed straight from the trailer.

Planned Farm Building

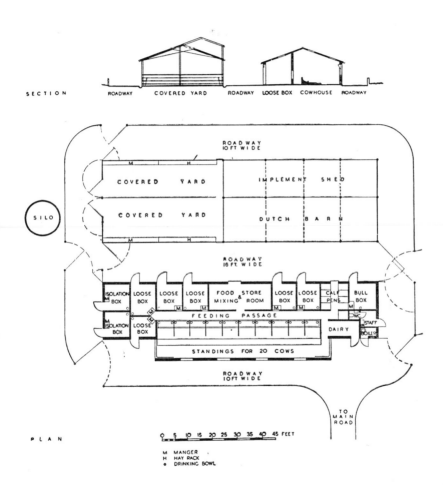

SECTION

ROADWAY COVERED YARD ROADWAY LOOSE BOX COWHOUSE ROADWAY

ROADWAY
10 FT WIDE

| SILO | COVERED | YARD | IMPLEMENT | SHED |
| | COVERED | YARD | DUTCH | BARN |

ROADWAY
16 FT WIDE

| ISOLATION BOX | LOOSE BOX | LOOSE BOX | LOOSE BOX | FOOD MIXING & STORE ROOM | LOOSE BOX | LOOSE BOX | CALF PENS | BULL BOX |

FEEDING PASSAGE

| ISOLATION BOX | LOOSE BOX | | | | | | DAIRY | STAFF / WC / BOILER |

STANDINGS FOR 20 COWS

ROADWAY
10 FT WIDE

TO
MAIN
ROAD

PLAN

0 5 10 15 20 25 30 35 40 45 FEET

M MANGER
H HAY RACK
○ DRINKING BOWL

27

Generally speaking a farmer is entitled to erect without town and country planning permission any farm building provided it is not less than 80′ from a main road and, in the words of the Act, 'provided it is properly designed for its purpose'.

But there are many snags. For example, a nissen hut can be properly designed – from the farming point of view – as a cow-house. But it is doubtful whether a town and country planning officer would pass it if the intention was to erect it in public sight.

If, however, the intention was to erect it where it could not be seen by the public, then he would probably say that planning permission was unnecessary in any case.

BEWARE LOCAL BYE-LAWS

The local council authorities are not so concerned with planning aspects in relation to local bye-laws. But they are concerned with building proposals, especially if main water and main sewerage is involved.

For example, you need their permission to connect to a local water main or to a main sewer. You also need their permission to carry a drain under a public road. In fact, any system of drainage needs the approval of the sanitary inspector of the local authority.

So it is a wise precaution to see the town and country planning officer (his office is usually in the county or borough council offices) about *any* new building proposal or any major exterior alteration to an existing building and to ask him whether planning permission is necessary or not.

If it is not necessary, all well and good. You can then ask at the local council offices whether they will have any concern in the proposals. If they have not, you have the all-clear to go ahead.

WHEN ARCHITECTS' PLANS ARE NECESSARY

But if local council approval is necessary you will have to submit properly-drawn plans to them. And if town and country planning permission is also necessary, you will have to submit those plans in duplicate, possibly in triplicate. The local council will advise you on this point.

Unless you are expert at drawing up plans you will have to get an architect (or possibly someone engaged in plan drawing for a living) to do this job.

But if you are proposing to do the building yourself or to do it with farm labour, make sure that the person you ask to draw up the plans understands your intentions.

EMPLOYING AN ARCHITECT

Normally an architect designs buildings in consultation with his client. Then he gets the plans passed and supervises the construction. For these services he charges a percentage of the total cost (the percentage depends on the size of the job) plus all expenses he incurs.

So it is wise to explain exactly what you propose to do and to say that you simply wish the plans to be drawn up according to your proposals and then handed back to you. You may find some architects unwilling to work on this basis.

It is also wise to be sure that you have thought out your proposals fully before you put final plans in hand. 'Afterthoughts' cost extra; new plans have to be drawn up for resubmission to the authorities.

When the final plans have been prepared they should be submitted to the local, urban or rural district council. After approval, they should be sent on to the planning authority – you can obtain the necessary application form from the council offices.

When you get final planning approval you can go ahead with the job.

CHAPTER III

CHOOSING THE MATERIALS
FOR THE JOB

A LL the time you are thinking about and planning a new
building you will have to bear in mind the kinds of
materials you will eventually use.

The suitability of alternative materials will have to be compared,
and so will costs. To do this you will need to make provisional
estimates of the quantities required. These, in turn, will be a guide
to drawing up your final order.

I have already suggested the advisability of using frame buildings wherever possible because of the ease with which they can be
converted to alternative uses. With such buildings the first step is
to decide the type of frame desired.

ADVANTAGE OF STEEL FRAMES

Steel is perhaps the most common today. It has the advantage
of long life; its initial cost is not much greater than for other frame
materials.

In buying a steel frame it is best to get quotations from several firms and to enquire how long they need for delivery. Prices and delivery dates vary considerably, so enquiries are well worth while.

When asking for quotations it is necessary to state what materials you propose to use for walls and roofing, so that the appropriate type of stanchion and girder is supplied.

LIGHTER ROOFS – LIGHTER GIRDERS

A roof that is to be clad with corrugated steel sheets will be much lighter than if, say, asbestos cement sheets are used, and the section of steel used in the roof construction can be lighter.

In the case of walls to a barn, it requires quite heavy angle-iron if asbestos cement sheets are to be 'hung' with a space below. But if there is to be a dwarf wall to carry the weight the angles can be lighter.

It is also necessary to let the manufacturers know whether the stanchions are to be fitted with base plates for bolting to the foundations or whether they are to be set into the ground or concrete.

Most suppliers of steel frames will undertake their erection if required. But the cost is not cheap, as the men's travelling and boarding expenses have to be paid as extras.

Provided there are one or two people on the farm who do not mind working on a height from the ground and are reasonably intelligent, then the job of erecting steel frames can be confidently tackled. The principles to be followed are outlined in the next chapter.

CONCRETE BUILDING FRAMES

Next to steel, I suppose reinforced and prestressed concrete frames are in order of popularity.

Prestressed concrete is the result of a new technique evolved during the last few years. It is essentially a factory method, as design and construction need expert knowledge. But the result is

31

lighter and tougher sections than are possible through ordinary reinforcing.

An ordinary reinforced beam will, under load, tend to bend, with the result that slight cracks will appear on the bottom side. This is caused by a slight stretching of the steel reinforcement. Its extent will depend, naturally, on the position of the beam and on the load it carries. Often it is of no importance.

PRESTRESSING AVOIDS CRACKS

But prestressing eliminates the risk. In its manufacture the steel reinforcement rod is replaced by cold-drawn wire of high tensile strength. The wire is stretched between anchors, then good quality concrete is poured into the mould through which it runs. The moulds are vibrated and the concrete is 'cured' under controlled conditions.

When the concrete is cured the wire is cut at the ends; it attempts to regain its original length and in doing so causes the concrete to compress along its whole length.

When the prestressed beam takes a load, it is impossible for the reinforcing to stretch as in the ordinary beam, and so no cracks will develop.

Many firms are now making prestressed sections; with them the erection of almost any building is within the capacity of any farmer and his staff, particularly when much of the lifting can be done by a jib replacing the fork on a high-lift mounted muck fork.

Again the point of asking for prices and delivery dates should be borne in mind; also the possibility of using manufacturers' stock sizes and the need for stipulating the kind of materials you will be using to clad the walls and roof.

USING TIMBER FRAMES

The other possible material for frames of buildings is timber.

Wartime shortage of timber, together with high costs, resulted in a considerable set-back in the use of timber for buildings. Today there is more timber available, but the cost of imported supplies is still six times greater than pre-war, whereas other materials are only about three times their pre-war costs.

However, home-grown timber has fallen considerably in price, and it may well be that – in the near future – it can be used to give reasonably priced buildings.

STUDY NEW METHODS

Certainly the newer methods of building in timber, as evolved by the Timber Development Association, should be studied – for example, the use of steel timber connectors. The photograph facing page 41 shows a timber-built dutch barn which was erected for test purposes in 1953. The clear headroom will be noted; it is achieved through the new technique.

At the 1954 Royal Show there was a development of this. A barn exhibited there had a light collar high up under the ridge and had simplified corners. This should, no doubt, reduce the cost but not the strength.

So building in timber should not be ruled out; indeed there is every reason to include it at the estimating stage and to make your final decision on the grounds of cost. You can reckon that in convenience and in length of life a timber-framed building should compare favourably with one in any other material – except perhaps when a second storey is required.

MATERIALS FOR WALLS

For walls there is a choice of several materials – bricks, concrete blocks, interlocking blocks used without mortar, and concrete panels. Another alternative is concrete poured into wooden shuttering or applied layer by layer by a specially devised piece of equipment.

Except in circumstances where the walls are unlikely to be subjected to hard knocks, it is inadvisable to clad walls in sheeting,

c

particularly the rather brittle asbestos sheeting. A low wall of bricks or blocks with sheeting above it is safer where there is traffic about.

There are a number of types of bricks. The most common is the Fletton which can be bought with grooves in one side to make a key for facing, or with a rusticated side with wavy markings which give a more pleasing appearance to a wall.

If you are particularly anxious about the looks of a building, go to a local supplier and see what he can offer. He may have something particularly suitable for the district.

BUYING BRICKS . . .

There is a considerable price range for bricks. The quotation is usually at a price per 1,000. Full lorry loads, with a minimum normally of 3,500 bricks, come cheaper per 1,000 than smaller quantities.

The common size of brick is $9'' \times 4\frac{1}{4}'' \times 2\frac{3}{8}''$, but the thickness varies with different types and makes. The thinner bricks are used chiefly for decoration.

As a rough guide to the number of bricks required, it takes twenty-three courses of $2\frac{3}{8}''$-thick bricks with $\frac{1}{2}''$ mortar joints to make a wall 6' high, and it takes thirteen bricks in each course to make a 10' length of wall.

So, if a wall is to be 3' high and 40' long, it requires 12 ($\frac{1}{2} \times 23$) $\times$ 52 (4 $\times$ 13) bricks, i.e. 624 for a wall one-brick wide. For a wall two bricks wide – they usually are – the number of bricks necessary would be 1,248. That gives 120 square feet – approximately ten and a half bricks per square foot.

. . . AND BLOCKS

Concrete blocks are generally more expensive to buy than bricks but they are cheaper to lay with farm labour than bricks. When the ultimate cost of the two methods is totted up, there's not much in it.

But concrete blocks do allow for much faster work than when

using bricks, an average-sized block covering the same area as half a dozen bricks. And, of course, less mortar is required.

There are two main types of blocks available – dense and lightweight. Both kinds are available as solid or hollow blocks.

The dense concrete blocks are made from a normal concrete mix. Lightweight blocks incorporate material such as clinker, foamed slag, pumic, etc., or are aerated mechanically or chemically before setting.

The dense-ballast aggregate blocks are suitable for all load-bearing work, whereas clinker blocks are ideal for internal partition walls, etc.

'Leca' blocks weigh about half the weight of dense blocks but can be used for load-bearing and they have excellent thermal and sound insulation properties. They are often used for porous floors to corn bins, but it must be borne in mind that over a period of time they do tend to fill up with dust.

WORKING OUT BLOCK QUANTITIES

Blocks of both types are made in a variety of thicknesses. But bear in mind that with concrete blocks the quoted size usually includes an allowance for the thickness of the joints. Thus a block with an actual size of $17\frac{5}{8}'' \times 8\frac{5}{8}'' \times 8\frac{3}{4}''$ is referred to by its nominal size of $18'' \times 9'' \times 9''$.

To work out the quantity of blocks you will require for a given length of wall is quite simple, as all blocks have a nominal surface dimension of $18'' \times 9''$ and so, irrespective of thickness, eight blocks are required for each square yard of walling.

In addition to the ordinary concrete blocks, there is another type called dri-crete blocks.

These are interlocking blocks which are erected on normal foundations but with only the first course bedded on mortar. The following courses are laid dry. Besides the obvious economy in mortar, these blocks are particularly suitable for erection by farm labour.

A number of firms make dri-crete blocks and will quote for the number of blocks required to do a particular job.

Walls can also be erected from concrete panels, and details of standard types available from local works would be well worth getting. As far as I know there has been no attempt to make these to a British Standard Specification as in the case of blocks.

Finally, concrete walls can be made in situ with shuttering instead of with pre-cast blocks. Using a semi-dry concrete mix, this is a particularly economic method of walling, especially for making fill-in walls between concrete or steel uprights.

BUYING AND STORING CEMENT

All these methods of wall-building – which are explained in detail in subsequent chapters – involve the use of concrete in some form or another so that the next job is to select and buy the materials needed to make up the concrete.

Concrete, as is well known, is made up of a mixture of cement and sand, gravel or stone.

Cement is obtainable as ordinary Portland cement or rapid-hardening. The Portland takes twenty-eight days to reach full strength, the rapid-hardening attains that strength in three days. The rapid-hardening, which is more finely ground, costs more than Portland.

When storing cement, remember that setting will start to take place in the bags if they are not kept perfectly dry. Always store on wood in a dry building.

Even when stored under these conditions 'air set' may take place in damp weather, the moisture going through the bags. If this does happen the cement can still be used as long as the lumps can be broken down with the fingers.

SAND SHOULD BE CLEAN

In buying sand it is necessary to see that it is clean, that it is free from mud and clay. More often than not it is washed and so is clean.

You can buy sharp sand or soft sand – the latter being used, at least as a proportion, in mortar for bricklaying. If you have only sharp sand in the mortar, it is difficult to make it 'butter' on the bricks and it will not hold on the trowel.

It is usual to have both sharp and soft sand delivered and mixed with the cement in proportions to make it work comfortably for the job in hand.

SELECTING THE RIGHT GRAVEL

Gravel, for most purposes, must be screened. Three-quarter-inch gravel is the normal size, being graded down from $\frac{3}{4}''$ down to $\frac{3}{16}''$. Bigger sizes can be used on some work, but no particle should be of greater diameter than one-quarter of the thickness of the work in hand.

For foundations and similar work you can cut down costs by using all-in ballast. This is gravel just as excavated from the pit and not screened and is therefore cheaper.

All you need to watch in buying gravel or stone is that you have no soft materials mixed in with it. Lumps of clay can appear hard when dry but they are useless in concrete.

These materials are used in different proportions for particular jobs. The mixtures are always referred to as a ratio, for example 4 : 2 : 1. This indicates that there are four parts of gravel, two parts sand and one part cement. Another example is a 6 : 1 mix. This indicates six of gravel or sand to one of cement. The figure for cement is always placed last.

SUITABLE CONCRETE MIXES

Mixing is usually done by volume of gravel and sand to weight of cement. A cubic foot of cement weighs 90 lb.

The following are the main mixes likely to be required for farm building:

Foundations. 6 : 1 mix of all-in ballast and cement. A cubic yard of this mix would consist of 31 cwt ballast and 4 cwt cement. One cubic yard should be sufficient for 17' of 2' wide, 9" deep foundation.

Mortar for brickwork. 6 : 1 mix of sand and cement. A cubic yard of this mix would be made up of 25 cwt sand and 4 cwt cement. For all but the strongest brickwork, lime is usually used in place of, or in addition to, the cement in this mix. It takes about one cubic yard of mortar for every 2,000 bricks laid with half-inch joints.

Mortar for concrete blocks. The mixture is exactly the same as that required for brickwork, but it requires only about half the quantity as compared with that required for the same area of brickwork.

Mortar for rendering. Six parts clean sharp sand, one part cement and one part hydrated lime is a good workable mix. In making mortar for rendering it is a common mistake to make the mixture too strong. The stronger the mixture the greater is the chance of shrinkage taking place, with the consequent formation of cracks.

It is advisable to put water on the wall before starting rendering. Dry bricks will draw the water from the mortar and you will not get a really good 'key' to the wall.

If you are rendering a wall 6' long, 10' high and putting 1" of rendering, you will use 5 cubic feet of material – which weighs about 7 cwt. So it is essential that you do get a good joint to the brickwork. This can be done by using considerable force in applying the coat of mortar. Do not over-trowel; once the surface is level leave it alone, as too much trowelling will cause cracks.

Concrete floors. A rough guide to quantities required for a cubic yard can be obtained from the following:

MIXTURE			WEIGHT REQUIRED		
Shingle	*Sand*	*Cement*	*Shingle*	*Sand*	*Cement*
3	2	1	20 cwt	10 cwt	5 cwt
5	3	1	22 cwt	10 cwt	3½ cwt

Using all-in ballast, the quantities would be:

MIXTURE		WEIGHT REQUIRED	
Ballast	Cement	Ballast	Cement
3	1	31 cwt	8 cwt
5	1	31 cwt	5 cwt
6	1	31 cwt	4 cwt
8	1	31 cwt	3 cwt

One cubic yard equals 27 cubic feet; that amount of concrete will cover an area $12' \times 9'$ to a depth of $3''$.

Semi-dry mix for walls. The quantities required for this method of building walls can be got from the above table.

CHAPTER IV

PREPARING AND
MARKING OUT THE SITE

I F an old building has to be demolished to make room for the new one, remember that much of the material may be useful or that it may be saleable. Slates, tiles, sheeting, timber, window-frames and doors should be removed with care for this reason. Their value makes it worth while drilling out pegs and hacksawing through rusted-in nails, screws and bolts.

Old bricks which were built with lime mortar are well worth cleaning up as it is not difficult to clean them with a bricklayer's trowel or with a bricklayer's bolster and hammer.

The latter may be necessary if the mortar is set rather hard on the bricks.

If the wall was built with cement mortar it is doubtful if it will be worth while trying to clean them, the cost of cleaning each brick would be more than the cost of a new one. However they will make useful hardcore and should be kept together ready for that purpose.

Plan the demolition in an orderly fashion so that all salvaged material is well clear of the site. Burn what rubbish you can; any

A bulldozer makes an effective job of
rough site levelling. One can be hired,
or the job can be given to a contractor.

For lighter levelling jobs (or for
finishing off after bulldozing) an earth
mover is a useful tool.

Materials should be accurately measured (note the box in the photograph; it measures internally 1′ × 1′ × 1′ and holds a cubic foot) and thoroughly mixed.

The Right Way

Turn the heap at least three times. When thoroughly mixed in the dry state, scoop out the centre ready for the water.

Use rather less than the full quantity of water required at this stage. Have handy a watering can with a rose for adding the extra water during mixing.

to Mix Concrete

Throw in material from the outside of the heap and ensure it mixes thoroughly with the water. Turn the mixture at least three times before using.

Mixing

This mixture contains too much large aggregate and insufficient cement and sand. It will give a rough and pitted surface.

Wrong

This has the opposite fault, there is insufficient aggregate, too much cement and sand. The resultant concrete may be porous; it will certainly be more expensive than necessary.

Concrete

When a mixture is just right it will, on trowelling, give a smooth surface, and the aggregate will be well bound with cement and sand. It will give a strong concrete.

Right

A good test is to squeeze a handful of the wet mixture. Moisture should come to the surface but there should be no excess of it to drip off.

Some Concrete Mixers

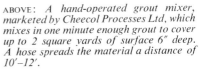

ABOVE: *The Benford (Benford Ltd) mobile concrete mixer driven by Villiers petrol engine. It has an output of 3 cubic feet per batch.*

ABOVE: *A hand-operated grout mixer, marketed by Cheecol Processes Ltd, which mixes in one minute enough grout to cover up to 2 square yards of surface 6″ deep. A hose spreads the material a distance of 10′–12′.*

ABOVE: *A portable cement mixer, petrol engine driven and with manual tipping device.*

LEFT: *The Tamkin mounted concrete mixer which attaches to three-point linkage and works from pto shaft. Concrete can be mixed while the tractor is travelling, capacity is 3 cubic feet, wet.*

Front-mounted loader with jib attachment being used to raise steel frame span into position ready for bolting to stanchions.

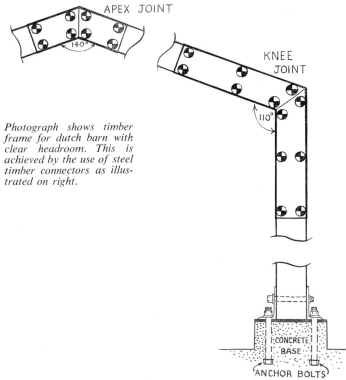

APEX JOINT

140°

KNEE
JOINT

110°

Photograph shows timber frame for dutch barn with clear headroom. This is achieved by the use of steel timber connectors as illustrated on right.

CONCRETE
BASE

ANCHOR BOLTS

rubble can be kept on the site for use in the foundations or under the floor of the new building.

If the old building had drains which are no longer required, they must be filled in. If there is insufficient rubble for this on the site, it will be necessary to obtain hardcore for the purpose. The job must be done properly otherwise the new building may be weakened.

Where old drains are still to be kept in use but pass under the site of the new building, the local authority may insist on their being diverted. If the local authority does not require this, they will need to be replaced by cast-iron pipes to prevent risk of broken pipes.

REMOVING TREES AND BUSHES

On entirely new sites there may be bushes or trees to remove before levelling can begin.

The smallest bushes can be pulled out by tractor. But see that the pulling chain is hitched to the tractor drawbar, not to the back axle. Hitching to the axle is bad for the tractor and it is dangerous. It may cause the tractor to rear and possibly even come over backwards.

Larger bushes and small trees will need a bulldozer, and the job is possibly best done by a contractor. Trees which need careful felling and, may be, the removal of stumps and roots by explosives, should be left to expert timber fellers, especially if near existing buildings. Sometimes local quarrymen will take on the job of blowing out stumps and roots.

Once these natural obstacles have been dealt with, the final stages of site preparation can be tackled.

DEALING WITH THE TOP-SOIL

The first job is to remove the top soil. Where the site is level enough for ploughing, the turf can be ploughed and the top soil loaded onto a trailer for removal right away from the site. A lot of hand work can be saved here if you have a front-mounted scoop and fit it to a mounted muck fork.

After the top soil has been removed, further levelling – if necessary – can be done by first ploughing the subsoil and then moving it by scoop from the higher to the lower parts. Remember that the loose soil will sink; consequently it should be built up higher and should be subjected to plenty of consolidation by the tractor.

In cases where the natural contours make ploughing impossible, either to remove the turf or to loosen the subsoil, a bulldozer will be the best implement to employ. It should be set to move the top soil first – again this can be loaded from a heap onto trailers by using a front-mounted scoop fitted to a mounted muck fork – then it should be used to level and consolidate the subsoil.

Of course, where a retaining wall or loading ramp is required, this should be built before the earth is moved. Then the soil should be packed tightly against it.

Finally, where circumstances allow, it is a good plan to level a site a little in excess of the actual building site. If an extra yard all round is levelled, working conditions will be easier.

TAKING LEVELS

When the site has been roughly levelled in this way and thoroughly consolidated, the next job is to take exact levels and mark out the site ready for foundation work.

For getting exact levels a surveyor's instrument – the dumpy level – is really only necessary on large jobs. For many farm buildings levels can be obtained by driving pegs in at, say, 10' intervals both up and down and across the site and getting the tops of these pegs level – they should be about 1' out of the ground – by checking with a straight board and a spirit level.

The board must be straight!

To set out the site it is almost essential to have a linen tape. This will enable you to get accurate right angles for the corners.

It is usually convenient to take the measurements of the buildings as being outside measurements, but if certain internal measurements

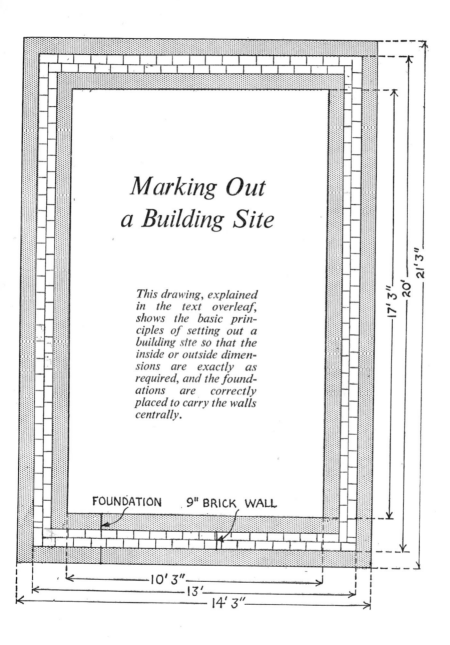

Marking Out
a Building Site

This drawing, explained in the text overleaf, shows the basic principles of setting out a building site so that the inside or outside dimensions are exactly as required, and the foundations are correctly placed to carry the walls centrally.

FOUNDATION   9" BRICK WALL

17' 3"
20'
21' 3"

10' 3"
13'
14' 3"

are required it is simply a matter of adding the width of the walls.

For example, a building which is to be 11′ 6″ × 18′ 6″ internally and is to be built of 9″ brickwork will have outside measurements of 13′ × 20′. And the foundations, extending 1′ each side of the centre line of the walls, will have outside measurements of 14′ 3″ × 21′ 3″.

The site will need to be marked out a little larger than this, so first peg out and square up an area of say 16′ × 24′.

Measure out, say, 12′ from a corner post along one side of the site. Along the other side measure out 16′ then measure diagonally

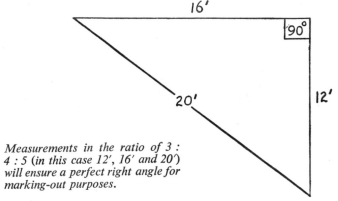

Measurements in the ratio of 3 : 4 : 5 (in this case 12′, 16′ and 20′) will ensure a perfect right angle for marking-out purposes.

across from the 12′ mark to the 16′ mark. The diagonal must be 20′ long to give an exact right angle at the corner.

You can take longer or shorter measurements according to the size of the building, but you must always work to the ratio of 3 : 4 : 5.

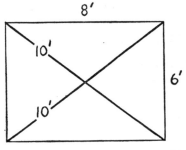

For small buildings it is an easy matter to measure both diagonals; if they are the same, the corners are right angles.

44

In the case of a small building the squareness of the corners can be checked by measuring the two diagonals. They should, of course, be the same.

With the 'working area' pegged out in this way the really careful pegging of the site can begin.

In the case of the example I have been quoting, the outside measurements of the foundations were 14' 3" × 21' 3" and these sizes should now be pegged out exactly within the squared-up area of 16' × 24', making sure that the corners are again properly checked for right angles. It does not matter about having these pegs level, as the depth of the foundation will be taken from the first levelling pegs.

Then take the width of the foundation – in this case 2' – and measure that width all the way round inside the last lot of pegs, placing another row of pegs in position.

The space between the two rows of pegs now marks the exact position and width of the trenches that will have to be dug for foundations.

45

CHAPTER V

LAYING DRAINS

IF the new building is one which requires drains, these should be laid before digging out and concreting the foundations. Similarly, any diversion of old drains should be undertaken at this stage.

Here it must be remembered that any system of drainage, except one dealing with rain-water only, must comply with the requirements of the local authority. Thus it is wise to consult their bye-laws or, preferably, to get the sanitary inspector's approval of your proposals.

In most areas it will, in any case, be necessary to have the actual work passed by the sanitary inspector before the trenches are finally filled in.

WHEN DRAINS RUN TO DITCH

If the pipes are to empty into an open ditch or drain, it is important to have the opening above what you consider the normal winter water level – otherwise the pipes will not run freely during times of heavy rain.

Putting down a simple system like this is quite straightforward.

The drain trench should be started at the lower end; it should, I recommend, be deep enough to allow for a 4″ layer of concrete all along the bottom as a bed for the pipes. This may seem rather expensive, but on most land is well worth while as it ensures no settlement of the pipes after filling and saves somebody – perhaps not you! – the job of relaying the drains in the future.

The fall depends on the size of pipe used. It should be 1′ in 30′ for 3″ pipes; 1′ in 40′ for 4″ pipes; 1′ in 50′ for 5″ pipes and 1′ in 60′ for 6″ pipes. For most farm building jobs 4″ pipes will be quite satisfactory for branch drains; main drains require 6″ pipes.

HOW TO LAY THE PIPES

Glazed pipes should be used, and work should start at the lower end of the drain, placing each pipe so that the collar end is away from the drain outlet.

As each pipe is laid, place a block of wood or half a brick underneath it, near the spigot end. This will keep the pipe level and make room for your hands when jointing.

If a tarred hemp gasket is wrapped round the spigot end before it is inserted into the collar of the previous pipe, it will help to

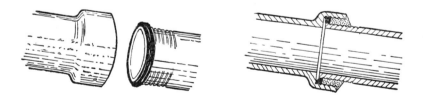

Tarred hemp gasket – (left) on spigot end before insertion, (right) after pipes have been jointed.

locate the join and will also prevent the jointing mortar from getting into the pipes.

If you do not use gaskets, see that the inside of each pipe is scraped clean before laying the next. A handy tool for this can easily be made. All that is needed is a short wooden handle and a semi-circle of metal or wood – as this sketch shows.

A setting-out line should run down the centre of the pipes. But do not use it as a guide to fall, as it is bound to sag.

For the mortar jointing use a mixture of one part cement to one part sand. Mix it stiff, otherwise it will tend to run round the curved surface of the joint.

Once the trenches have been dug for drains it is advisable to complete the work without delay. Open trenches will impede traffic and transport of material to the site; they may flood, and the sides may fall in – all of which makes a lot of unnecessary work.

More complicated systems of drainage will involve the same basic principles, but additional constructional jobs are called for.

BUILDING INSPECTION CHAMBERS

Inspection chambers are needed where pipe junctions occur; liquid manure tanks may be required, sometimes to take rain-water as well, but it is a great mistake to do this. It is far better to have separating chambers or independent drains to separate rain-water from urine.

Inspection chambers should be at least 2′ 6″ square internally so that there is room to manœuvre 2′ lengths of drain rod into them when necessary. They should also be not more than 5′ deep except where circumstances make this absolutely necessary. Walls should preferably be of 9″ brickwork, or concrete blocks. If bricks are used, they should be rendered on the outside so that surface water will not enter the chamber; if concrete blocks are used, they are best surrounded with 5″ or 6″ of poured concrete, a 6: 3: 1 mixture will do.

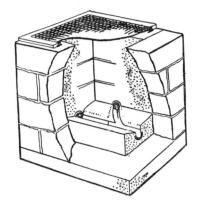

Cutaway section of inspection chamber shows detail of construction.

Finally, the inspection chamber walls should be built on a concrete base about 6″ thick.

Therefore, to allow for ease in construction, a hole some 5′ square needs to be excavated.

The 6″ concrete raft should, of course, be laid perfectly horizontal and not follow the fall of the drain – otherwise there will be difficulty in building the walls. But the open channels – formed by setting half-round pipes in concrete – must follow the drain fall.

In the case of side channels joining a main drain, the angle of the side drain is curved where it enters the main so that, as nearly as possible, the flow of the side drain is turned in the direction of the flow of the main drain.

The concrete benching in which these half-round pipes are set should slope down to the channel at a fall of about 1″ in 6″.

The methods of building the walls, either in bricks or blocks, can be found by referring to chapter VIII.

FITTING COVERS

When the walls are completed, cover the full width of them at the top with cement mortar (6 : 1 mixture) and bed the cover frame into this bedding. Keep the lid in position while you do so; this will prevent any distortion of the frame.

It is possible to make one set of drainage pipes deal with liquid manure as well as rain-water and, where necessary, washing-down water. This can be done in several ways:

1. Where a natural slope allows it, the pipes can empty into an open channel-work of shallow ditches which distribute the water and urine over a limited section of one field.

   Except on grounds of low initial cost, there is little to commend this system, particularly as the field is likely to be a home paddock which will already have a lot of locked-up fertility. And, because it will carry stock, the ditches are bound to need fairly constant attention if they are to keep functioning properly.

2. Rain-water, washing-down water and urine can be led to one large storage tank from which the highly-diluted contents can be pumped either direct to irrigation pipes or, at intervals into a mobile liquid manure tank or sprayer for distribution in the fields.

3. The drainage system can be interrupted by a separating chamber which will divert the liquid manure first into a settling tank and then into a small storage tank from which it can be pumped as required, leaving the water to run into a larger tank or to a ditch or open drain.

VALUE OF DOUBLE-DRAIN SYSTEM

I think it is preferable, where the liquid manure is to be conserved, to have a double-drainage system, with one set of pipes taking the liquid manure to a settling tank and then on to a storage tank and another set of pipes dealing with the water.

In this case a double-drain gulley will be necessary outside the building. It will have two grids – one to the drain for urine and one to the water drain. The separation of the two liquids can be achieved either by using a movable cover for the grids or by arranging a separating device in the gulley.

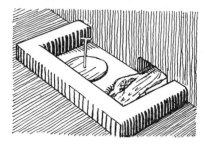

When separating device is arranged in gulley the cover needs to be moved to allow liquids to enter correct drain.

Where a movable cover is used it is normally placed over the water drain grid, except when the building interior is being washed down; then the cover is put over the liquid manure drain grid to prevent water from flowing to the urine tank.

The disadvantage of this system is that you cannot have the down-pipe from the rain-water guttering emptying into the gulley; if you did, there would be many occasions when rain-water would flow into the liquid manure drain.

Consequently this system involves having a separate gulley for rain-water and a separate short drain from this gulley joining up with the washing-down water drain.

For this reason I prefer the use of a separating device at the double gulley.

It is a simple device, as the sketch shows. The washing-down water, because of its strong flow, rushes over the 'weir' into one

drain; the liquid manure, usually no more than a trickle, falls short of the 'weir' into the other drain.

Not only does this eliminate the need for remembering to

51

manipulate a cover, it enables you to bring the guttering down-pipes to discharge into the same drain as the washing-down water. This saves having to have a special gulley and short drain for the rain-water.

METHODS OF URINE COLLECTION

According to which method of liquid manure collection you choose, you will need to build into the drainage system one or more of the following:

a large storage tank for water and urine,
a separating chamber,
a settling tank,
a liquid manure tank.

The drawings on the facing page show the different arrangements that are possible.

BUILDING A SEPARATING CHAMBER

Constructional principles for a separating chamber, settling chamber and liquid manure tank are much the same as for an inspection chamber. The main differences are in size (appendices II and III give tables for determining the size of drainage tank installations) and the fact that the walls of these chambers and tanks must be impervious on the inside.

Holes should be excavated large enough to allow for convenient working. Then a 6″ base of concrete should be laid. Include in the mixture one of the proprietary compounds for making concrete completely waterproof.

Build the walls in 9″ brickwork or concrete blocks, taking care that the inlet and outlet pipes are fitted in the proper positions. Then render the bricks or blocks with 1″ layer of a mixture of 6 : 1 sand and cement. This, too, should contain a waterproofing compound.

Three Methods of Drainage

1. Simple collection in one tank.

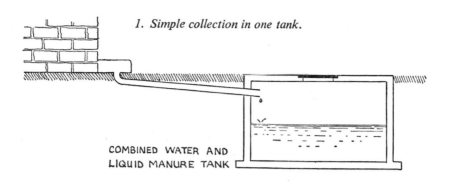

COMBINED WATER AND
LIQUID MANURE TANK

2. Using separating device at gulley (waste water going to ditch) with settling tank and liquid manure tank.

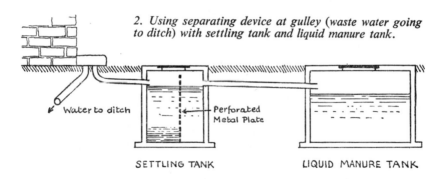

Water to ditch — Perforated Metal Plate

SETTLING TANK   LIQUID MANURE TANK

3. Using specially built separating chamber which diverts waste water to ditch and urine to storage tank.

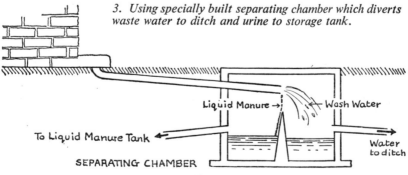

Liquid Manure →   ← Wash Water

To Liquid Manure Tank ←

Water to ditch

SEPARATING CHAMBER

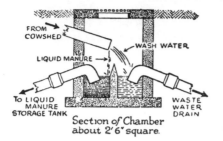

FROM COWSHED

WASH WATER

LIQUID MANURE →

To LIQUID MANURE STORAGE TANK

WASTE WATER DRAIN

Section of Chamber about 2' 6" square.

Detail of a separating chamber.

You will notice from the drawing that the separating chamber works on the principle I have already explained for separating liquid manure from washing-down water at a drain gulley. The inlet pipe is so placed over a knife-edged 'weir' that the urine, flowing at a trickle, falls to one side, while the gushing water flow falls to the other side.

The 'weir' can be constructed with a narrow concrete slab, set in situ between boards, or it can be precast and then set in the brickwork.

It is advisable to include perforated plates in the separating chamber to trap material which might otherwise block the system. Use flat steel sheeting with perforations of, say, $\frac{1}{4}''$ holes spaced $\frac{1}{2}''$ apart in each direction.

These plates need to be so placed that they can be easily taken out for cleaning. Ledges can be formed on the weir for them to rest on, with corresponding ledges on the concrete or brick walls.

The settling tank also requires a perforated plate. In this case it is, of course, placed vertically across the flow, fitting in grooves in the walls. These can be formed in the brickwork or concrete, or two pieces of angle iron can be built into the walls by drilling them and inserting bolts, thus:

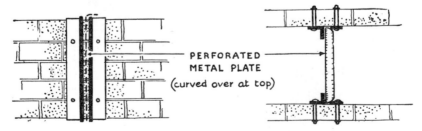

PERFORATED METAL PLATE (curved over at top)

54

If the top edge of the sheet is bent over it makes it stronger and easier to grasp for handling.

A SIMPLER ARRANGEMENT

It is sometimes convenient to build the settling chamber and manure tank together. This arrangement is shown below:

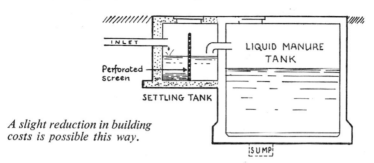

INLET

LIQUID MANURE TANK

Perforated screen

SETTLING TANK

A slight reduction in building costs is possible this way.

SUMP

Separating chambers, settling tanks and liquid manure tanks should all be provided with manhole covers.

One method of fitting these is to mould concrete slabs for the tops. They can be built quite simply.

MAKING CONCRETE COVERS

You need a level wooden platform and on this you should place a wooden frame of which the internal measurements equal the outside dimensions of the structure to be covered. The wooden frame should be the depth it is desired to make the manhole cover.

Make up a mortar of 5 : 1 sand and cement, put about 2″ in the frame and reinforce with expanded metal sheeting plus, if a large cover, some $\frac{3}{8}″$ round iron rod. Put a ring in the middle (supported to keep it clear of the mortar) and then fill the frame to the top.

When set, this slab can be put on the chamber.

You can, of course, use the cast-iron manhole covers and frames. They are not very expensive.

To fit these you simply place the frame in position in the wooden frame (having greased the groove into which the cover fits) and make up to the top of the frame with a 6 : 1 sand and cement mixture. It is best to have the cover on while you do this, as it ensures that the frame is not distorted.

CALCULATING TANK SIZES

Where for any reason it is decided to collect rain-water, washing-down water and liquid manure in one large storage tank, the dimensions will have to be carefully worked out, as the volume will be very great.

Appendix II will give you the volume of liquid manure to allow for according to the stock. Washing-down water (usually applicable only to cowsheds and parlours, but occasionally for pigs) will amount to fifty gallons per cow per week and perhaps two gallons per pig – that figure is low, because I do not think it advisable to wash pig houses except at long intervals.

Rain-water, which should be calculated on a peak month, will vary according to roof and/or yard area but it can be a very large volume and for that reason, except under unusual conditions, should not be mixed with the liquid manure.

One inch of rain is one hundred tons to the acre, somewhere about five gallons per square yard; 3″ of rain in a month is not unusual in most parts of the country so that would be fifteen gallons per square yard of roof or yard.

STRENGTHENING LARGE TANKS

Tanks to serve this purpose can be constructed on the same principles as already outlined. But it must be remembered that the pressure on the walls will be considerable. If such a tank is underground, the soil will have a buttressing effect, but naturally the thickness of the walls have to be sufficient to withstand a fair pressure.

Nine-inch walling would be sufficient for most underground tanks, but a very large one would probably be better with about 5″ of concrete (5 : 4 : 1 mixture) on the outside of the walls.

It is well worth trying to get storage tanks of this kind, including liquid manure tanks, below ground level wherever soil contour permits. Then a pipe can be run from a low point for quite a distance if necessary for emptying without pumping.

The advantage is that they can then be emptied by gravity into

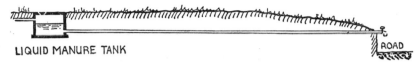

LIQUID MANURE TANK   ROAD

mobile spreading tanks or distributors. Thus the initial cost of a pump is eliminated; so is the cost of regular pumping, whether by hand or by machine.

Thus it may pay to run the drain pipes quite a distance to reach a soil level where the liquid can be drawn off.

CHAPTER VI

LAYING A GOOD FOUNDATION

YOU will recall that in the previous chapter but one I dealt with marking out the site of foundations. In this chapter I will explain how foundations should be laid.

The method will, of course, vary according to the type of building and the form of construction to be used. Framed buildings without side walls (for example, dutch barns) will only need some kind of foundation for the uprights. But for most other kinds of building, whether of frame construction or not, a continuous foundation will be necessary.

WHEN TRENCH IS UNNECESSARY

Let us deal first with the simplest form – providing foundations for stanchions only.

In this case there will be no need to excavate a trench all along the marked-out foundation site. It will only be necessary to dig holes where the stanchions are to be erected.

The first step is to measure accurately the width of the roof trusses and purlins which are supplied. They may not be exactly as you specified, and, if there is any variation, you must allow for this in the foundations and make whatever adjustments that are required. Quite obviously the distance between the stanchions at the base must be exactly the same as at the top, both along and across the building.

After making any corrections which are necessary, the holes for the foundations can be dug out.

DEPTH OF HOLES

The actual depth of the holes will depend upon the construction of the building, but the makers of the frame will be able to tell you how deep they consider the stanchions should be set in.

Suppose they say 3'; then to that depth must be added the thickness of the concrete raft on which the stanchion should rest – say 9". Thus each hole should be 3' 9" deep.

The depth can be checked by putting a board from one of the levelling pegs across the hole and, with the aid of a spirit level,

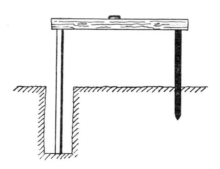

Method of establishing correct depth of a foundation hole.

checking that it is level and then measuring from the bottom of the board to the bottom of the hole.

Having got the hole the correct depth, drive a peg in to determine the top level of the concrete. Check this again off the levelling pegs and across the site to the other holes, as naturally all the pegs must be level with each other.

The concrete (9 : 1 gravel-as-dug and cement mix will do) is then poured into each hole. Some hardcore can be put in with it, but work it down well until the level of the peg is reached and leave the surface level.

When the concrete bases in all the holes have set, the stanchions should be set up, joined by the roof trusses, guyed with ropes and checked for uprightness and alignment. Then fill in round the stanchions with the same mix of concrete as the foundation; here again some hardcore can be worked in.

You can finish off at ground level or make a buttress round each stanchion by making a square box to fit round and filling it with concrete. The advantage of such buttresses in dutch barns is that they stop people driving tractors into the stanchions! At the same time they can get in the way!

MAKES DISMANTLING EASIER

When stanchions are sunk in the ground and concreted in position in this way, the job of dismantling – if it ever becomes necessary – is quite a problem. An alternative way, which would make dismantling and re-erection easier, is to use base plates to the stanchions and to bolt them to concrete foundations.

This is only possible with steelwork; concrete stanchions are set into the ground, and the modern way of erecting timber stanchions is to set steel into concrete and then bolt the timber to it. This has the advantage that you do not get rotting of the wood at ground level, and if it is necessary at some time to replace the timber it is simply a matter of bolting a new piece to the steel set in the concrete.

The foundation holes for concrete to carry base plates do not, naturally, have to be so deep as those required when stanchions are sunk into the foundations. But the blocks of concrete must be large enough to hold the building from lifting if the wind should get under the roof. Again it is a matter on which the frame manufacturer's advice should be sought.

The procedure for laying the foundations is as follows:

First make in thin sheet-metal or plywood a template to correspond to the base plate of the stanchion. This should show accurately the position of each hole and it should be marked with right-angle marks so that it can be squared up with the building site.

Drill out the holes in the template and put the bolts through them. Then apply the nuts and screw them down until the distance between each bolt head and nut equals the thickness of the base-plate plus the depth that the bolt heads are to be sunk in concrete.

When this is done, the foundation hole can be filled with concrete up to the point where the bolt heads are to be embedded. Use a mixture of nine parts gravel-as-dug with one part cement, and work in any suitable hardcore.

Then place the template in position with the bolt heads downwards and with the right-angle marks squaring with the pegged-out building site.

Check positioning exactly, then work concrete of the same mix round the bolt heads until the hole is filled up level with the bottom of the template.

The nuts and the template can be removed as soon as the concrete is set. If you are not satisfied that the face of the concrete is level, mix a little mortar – six parts sand, one cement – and correct with that.

Once the concrete is thoroughly dry, the stanchions can be lowered over the bolts and secured in position by the nuts.

When the stanchion bolts are embedded in the concrete foundations in this way, they are referred to as 'anchor' bolts. The building so erected will have considerable resistance to pressure from wind or other forces.

USING 'RAG' BOLTS

Where the structure is likely to have to bear a down load only, the use of 'rag' bolts is quite satisfactory. The method to employ with these is rather simpler.

The foundation hole can be filled with concrete (nine parts gravel-as-dug with one part cement), then greased timber pegs, about 3″ square should be plunged into the concrete in the approximate positions of the bolt holes.

When the concrete has set, these can be removed. The stanchions can then be raised into position with the rag bolts hanging down from the base plate and projecting into the holes. Support the

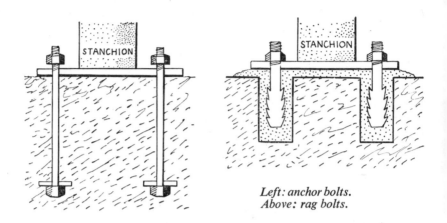

Left: anchor bolts.
Above: rag bolts.

stanchion about 1″ above the level of the concrete, then work a mortar of one part sand to one part cement down into the holes and under the base plate.

When the mortar is set, the nuts can be drawn tight.

A POINT TO WATCH

Where a frame building is to have stanchions dropped in the ground and concreted in position and is also to have walls, it is best to get the stanchions into place before digging out the foundation trench for the walls. Otherwise the work of erecting the stanchions is likely to cause some collapse of the trenches and involve a certain amount of re-digging.

But where stanchions are to be bolted to a concrete foundation which is also to carry the wall, then the foundation trench should, of course, be dug out completely, as it should also be for a building without framework.

The depth of a foundation trench depends on the nature of the soil and the weight to be carried. As a general rule it should be from 9″ to 12″ in sandy soils, about 9″ in gravel or clay and at least 6″ on rock.

If a building has to be erected on clays which are subject to expansion and contraction, then it is advisable to go down to a depth of at least 18″ to be sure of getting to a point where soil movement is almost nil. In this case it is not necessary to make foundations quite so wide as usual; 12″ will do.

TRENCH BOTTOM MUST BE LEVEL

The bottom of the trench must be level. To achieve this, cut the outside of the trench sheer against the marking pegs and take your depth from the levelling pegs. For example, if these pegs protrude 6″ above ground level and you are preparing a trench 9″ deep, then from the tops of the pegs to the bottom of the trench should measure 1′ 3″.

As a general rule the depth of the concrete foundation is equal to or perhaps just an inch or two less than the depth of the trench. But, of course, you must not use the ground-level to determine the line to which the top of the concrete must come.

To get an exact level – which is most important for subsequent building operations – the best way is to drive more wooden pegs down the centre of the trench. Space them about 10′ apart and let them protrude to whatever height the concrete foundation is to be.

This should be about 9″ for most building jobs, except where clay or rock make deeper or shallower foundations necessary. Small jobs – single pig sties for example – will not need more than 6″ in average soils.

The tops of these pegs must be accurately levelled by using a straight board and spirit level.

SAVING CONCRETE

Where there are plenty of stones or broken bricks available a considerable saving in concrete can be made by working in hardcore with the concrete. If you do this, the concrete must be well tamped down to ensure that the rubble is closely surrounded by it.

Concrete for foundations can be mixed from nine parts gravel to one part cement. The gravel can be what is called 'all-in' ballast, i.e. gravel taken just as it is excavated from the pit and not screened to remove sand, nor with added sand.

This is cheaper than screened material, but is quite suitable for trench foundations.

The concrete should be finished off reasonably smooth and must be levelled off exactly to the tops of the pegs in the trench.

Where steel stanchions with base plates are to be bolted to the foundations, then the necessary holes for rag bolts must be made or the anchor bolts must be set in the concrete before it is dry.

FOUNDATIONS ON SLOPING LAND

If foundations are to be put in on land which has a fall, steps are necessary in the foundations. You make each step so that when you come to build the wall it comes at the end of a brick or block and then the next course follows right through as shown in the sketch:

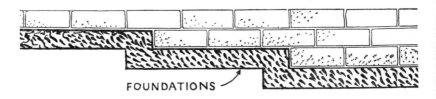

FOUNDATIONS

If foundations do have to come above ground-level at any point naturally it is necessary to set up shuttering.

HINTS ON CONCRETING

If you have any quantity of concreting to do it will pay to buy or hire a mixer. I have found the type that can be attached to the rear of a tractor very useful. It has the double advantage that when not in use there is no engine to depreciate, and it saves all barrowing of concrete – except in difficult positions.

The size of mixer is known by its capacity dry and wet. Thus one that is stated to be 5/3½ holds five cubic feet of dry material which, when it is placed in position, will be three and a half cubic feet of mixed concrete.

USING A MIXER

In using a mixer it is essential to get the correct proportions. Many textbooks tell you that to do this the gravel is placed in the drum first with the correct amount of water and then the sand and cement are added, but the more usual way – and certainly the quickest way – is to put water into the drum first and then cement followed by sand and shingle.

Again the textbooks tell you that every batch should be measured with a box without a bottom which, when filled level, gives an exact measure.

It is an excellent idea, but more suitable when mixing by hand. In the case of a machine the better way, as far as time is concerned anyway, is to measure one batch, very carefully noting the quantity of water required, and then – for subsequent batches – put the same quantity of water and add cement sand and gravel by counting the shovelfuls.

This should keep the mixture reasonably even. Any carelessness in the mix will show by the difference in colour as it is put down in position.

MIXING BY HAND

If mixing is done by hand, a clean level surface – either concrete or boards – is necessary; 8′ × 10′ is about the minimum area to work in comfort.

The mixture requires turning three times dry and twice wet which will give a uniform colour throughout the heap. This is slow and hard work and a mixer can be justified on these grounds on almost any building job.

E

It is essential that only clean water is used in mixing concrete and it is generally accepted that if the water is not fit to drink it is not fit for concrete.

The quantity of water that is added is very important. If the mixture is too wet – which does, it is true, make it easier to handle – the strength of the concrete will be far less than if the correct amount of water is used. A mixture which can be worked quite comfortably with a ratio of six gallons of water to one cwt of cement and which has a strength of 3,000 lb to the inch under compression will be reduced in strength to 2,300 lb if seven gallons are added and will drop right down to 1,800 lb if eight gallons have been used in the mix.

IF CONCRETE IS TOO DRY

On the other hand, if a mixture is too dry it is very difficult indeed to work down, and even with a lot of tamping there will remain air spaces and the concrete will not be a compact mass with every pebble surrounded by sand and cement.

Concrete which has the correct amount of water will have a glossy surface after it has set.

CHAPTER VII

ERECTING
A BUILDING FRAME

WHERE a building is being erected without a frame then, after laying the foundations, the work of bricklaying or block laying proceeds.

In such a case a reader should omit this chapter and turn straightway to chapter VIII which deals with the principles of bricklaying, etc.

But as so many buildings today are frame structures, this is the best stage to discuss the erection of the frame – the job that follows the laying down of foundations.

PRINCIPLES TO FOLLOW

Three types of frame structures were mentioned in chapter III. They were steel, concrete and timber. The principles of erection are very much the same in each case, but it is well to make sure that these principles are understood and that the various points of difference are known.

Consider the steel frame structure first.

I have already made a point about checking the sizes of the steel work and making any necessary adjustments in the foundations. This is particularly important; it is impossible to correct errors once the stanchions are concreted in position.

The best way to lift the steel stanchion which is either to be sunk into concrete or bolted to concrete foundations (as dealt with in the last chapter) is to use a high-lift front-mounted loader on a tractor.

Simply put a rope round the stanchion about 10′ from the bottom and tie this to the arm of the lift. Raise the lift and then drop it down gently into position.

WITHOUT EQUIPMENT

If you have not a front-mounted loader, it will take two or three people to do the job. First bolt – or tie – two pieces of wood together as shown in sketch and, when the top end of the stanchion

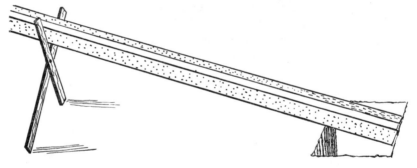

is lifted, slip this support underneath. As the stanchion is lifted higher and higher, so this is moved nearer the base.

PUTTING TRUSSES IN POSITION

Once the stanchions have been secured you can use the front-mounted loader to raise the roof trusses into position. The photograph between pages 40 and 41 shows this job being done. An angle iron extension to the loader had to be fitted owing to the apex of the truss being some 25′ above ground-level.

The truss was set up on the ground in the first place and was then lifted onto a trailer. After dropping it in an upright position the chains were taken off and the loader was let down to the ground again. The chains were then re-attached to enable the loader to lift the truss to the necessary height. With the truss held in position it was bolted to the stanchion.

BEST AND QUICKEST WAY

This is the best and quickest way to handle steel work today. The old method was to set up a pole with a pulley at the top and hoist up the various components by this means. The front-mounted loader, with a reasonably high lift, does the job more efficiently.

Once two adjacent roof trusses are in position, the purlins should be bolted into place.

This can best be done by having a man on each truss. The two of them can together draw up each purlin by ropes and quickly secure it in position.

If the stanchions are short or the trusses very strong it is possible to bolt the stanchions and trusses together on the ground and lift them both into position at the same time, guiding the stanchion bases into position.

USEFUL TOOL

No special tools are required for ordinary steel erection, but sometimes the use of a 'drift' is a great help. This is simply a round bar with a pointed end which can be put through the bolt holes if they do not line up ready for the bolt. You simply put it into the holes and lever them into line and, if necessary, put a carpenter's clamp on to hold the position while you slip the bolt through.

If the building is a two-storey structure, beams of the correct size will be supplied by the makers.

Whether these should be fitted to the stanchions before the roof trusses will depend upon the size of the building, but it would

The various parts of a concrete framework

probably in most cases be best to fit them before the trusses because, apart from anything else, they will give support to the stanchions and make some support for scaffold planks if you want to work on them.

If you wish to put an extra store into an existing building a guide to the necessary size of beam for different loads is given in appendix IV.

The method of fixing these in position is exactly as just outlined for a new building.

USING SECOND-HAND STEEL

One final point with regard to steel frames: if second-hand steel work is used it should be thoroughly cleaned down, and any holes which will not be used should be welded up. They can considerably weaken the strength of a member. Before erection the steel should have two coats of paint.

In erecting concrete frame buildings you are dealing with greater weights in many cases than for steel frames but the general principle is the same. The saving in time by the use of a high-lift loader is even more marked than in the steel frame because of this weight.

In the case of timber frames you need to use your discretion as to how much can be lifted together, but it has one advantage that you can, if necessary, put extra braces on by nailing lengths of timber to prevent twisting the frame while lifting.

Before leaving the question of frame buildings, mention should be made of the type of structure now available in which wall sheets and roof sheets of steel or asbestos provide almost all the whole of the strength in the building. No stanchions are required, the wall sheets being simply fixed to concrete foundations with brackets.

At the time of writing, such a building, complete with yoke or chain ties, water bowls, etc., works out at less than £25 per cow housed.

ADVANTAGE TO TENANT FARMERS

A building of this type has many advantages. Apart from being easy to erect, it is particularly suitable to a tenant-farmer in that it can be easily moved or disposed of as tenant right if he leaves the farm.

For most purposes I think asbestos cladding is much more satisfactory than steel for this kind of structure, but it must be kept in mind that asbestos sheeting is easily broken if driven into by tractors.

CHAPTER VIII

BUILDING IN
BRICKS AND BLOCKS

ANYONE can make a reasonably good job of bricklaying with a little care and attention. The secret of success lies in considering what you are setting out to do and then carefully, and probably slowly, getting on with the job.

Before attempting to lay any bricks it is essential to get clear in your mind the principle of bonding each layer of bricks.

Bonding ensures that the joints of one layer of bricks does not line up with the joints of the layer immediately above or below. If joints did line up in this way, there would be a weakness which might cause the wall to crack at the joints.

TWO TYPES OF BOND

There are a number of types of bond, but only two of them need concern us in farm-building work – the English Bond and the Stretcher Bond.

But before describing these two bonds I must explain that, in building terminology, bricks laid lengthwise are known as

72

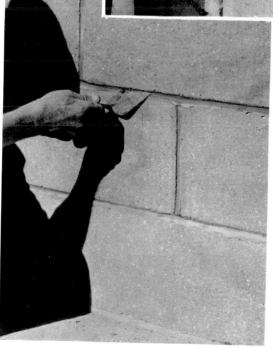

When laying blocks
put them on a bedding
of mortar; retrieve any
mortar which is squeezed
out, then – as bottom
picture shows – point
neatly with a trowel.

Top picture shows setting the formwork in position. It requires levelling (by spirit level) then tightening by the bolts so that it grips the framework.

Lower picture illustrates the method of filling with semi-dry concrete mix. This should be placed in 2″ layers.

Each 2″ layer of semi-dry mix should be tamped down firmly, as is being done in the left-hand photograph opposite.

Dry-Mix Wall

When the formwork has been filled in this way, the concrete should be levelled off by hammering on a block of wood. The formwork can then be removed, the bolt holes filled with concrete by trowel and the formwork placed higher up for a further layer.

The concrete wall should be lightly sprayed with water for a week or ten days so that it cures satisfactorily.

*A method of
renovating old clay
and plaster walls is
shown here.
It involves
applying expanded
metal to the old
walls and then
coating with cement
facing – two
applications, both
of one part cement
to three parts sand.*

*Top picture shows
the expanded metal.
Centre picture,
nailing the ex-
panded metal in
position. Picture
on the left shows
the completion
stage of an exterior
wall renovated in
this way.*

'stretchers'; when you can see the end of the brick it is known as a 'header'; half the width of a 'header' is called a 'closer'.

The English Bond consists of one layer of stretchers and one layer of headers alternately. Closers are inserted near the ends of

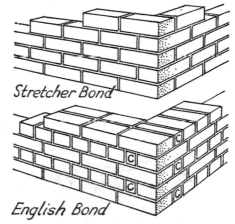

Stretcher Bond

The two main types of bond used in bricklaying. Note the 'closers'—marked C—in English Bond.

English Bond

the wall to make joints start correctly. The sketch shows what this type of bonding looks like.

This method of bonding gives the strongest type of 9" wall and saves nearly all cutting of bricks.

The Stretcher Bond is best for 4½" walling and consists solely of stretchers placed so that the joint of each brick comes at the centre of the brick immediately above and below it. As will be seen from the sketch no cutting of bricks is involved.

The tools required are:
Spirit level, 3' – 4' long, with levels for checking horizontal and vertical.
Bricklayer's trowel (blade about 12" long).
Pointing trowel (blade 3" – 6" long).
Bricklayer's bolster (a wide, cold chisel used for cutting bricks; cutting with a stroke of the trowel requires a lot of skill).
Lump hammer (short-handled hammer weighing 4 lb for use with bolster).
Bricklayer's line.

73

The first job is to mark out on your foundations the exact position for placing your first course of bricks.

You can do this by tying the line to a brick and extending it to two other bricks at adjacent corners. Check the squareness of the first corner. When all is square, start to lay bricks in that corner, working to the line. Repeat the procedure at another corner and see that the line is right from one corner to the next. Then you are all set for building up the two corners.

MORTAR FOR BRICKLAYING

Bricklaying mortar should be carefully mixed and should not be made too strong – six of sand to one of cement is ample. To make mortar too strong is not only expensive but may result in weakening the wall, as the mortar may be so strong that it will pull pieces out of the bricks.

The texture of the mixture should be such that it can be handled comfortably and will stick like butter to the end of the brick when laying.

Hydrated lime is often used to make mortar. It produces a fatty mortar which gives a good bond between brick and mortar. This hydrated lime is cheaper than cement but not so strong; it stiffens less rapidly and is not so frost resistant.

MIXTURES INCLUDING LIME

Suitable mixtures incorporating lime are – one hydrated lime to three of sand for ordinary work where no special weight is to be carried on the wall and where there is not much risk of frost damage. This mixture should not, however, be used below the damp course.

A mixture of one part cement, one non-hydrated lime and six sand is much more suitable. It is easy to handle and sets hard; it can be used when building in sandstone.

Remember that any mortar that has cement in it should be used within two hours of mixing.

Most building textbooks advise building the first courses of a wall wider than the actual wall itself. For a 9" wall, for example, the usual recommendation is for the first course to be 1' 6" wide and the next 1' 1½", the 9" work starting at the third course.

All this extra trouble is unnecessary if you have made good concrete foundations. You can start right from the first layer with 4½" or 9" work.

It should not be necessary to hammer a brick into position. Mortar should be spread evenly and about ½" thick on the bricks already in position. The brick to be laid should be buttered with ½" of mortar on one end (on the side if it is a header) and then slid against the preceding brick.

AVOIDING WASTE

Surplus mortar is pressed out and caught on the trowel ready to be applied to the next brick. Try not to let too much mortar drop. It's wasteful and makes the job look untidy.

When laying the first course of bricks you may find it necessary to make the bottom join between concrete foundation and brickwork a little thicker than the normal ½" as there is almost certain to be slight unevenness in the concrete.

Do make sure that this first course is level and that the angles at the corners are perfect right angles. The corner angles can be checked by using measurements of the ratio 3 : 4 : 5 as described in chapter IV.

After seeing the first course is level, one more course is laid. Then the damp course must be inserted.

LAYING THE DAMP COURSE

This can be of bitumen or of slates bedded in a strong concrete mixture but both must go right across the wall to make a complete barrier to damp. Bitumen is the cheaper of the two unless you have old slates to use up.

With slates, two layers have to be used to provide an overlap

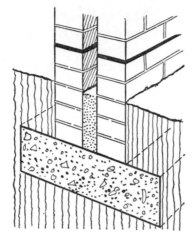

Sketch shows damp course to a cavity wall; for ordinary walls it extends right across the brickwork.

to the joints. With bitumen you unroll it direct onto a ½″ bed of mortar. There must be no cracks in the bitumen; old material is useless for this job. Where a joint has to be made in the felt there should be an overlap of at least 4″.

CARE AT THE CORNERS

You can now commence building the wall in earnest, starting by raising each corner by about ten courses.

Great care is needed in building up the corners to see that the thickness of the joints is correct and that the corner is upright and level. This is where the spirit level comes in.

As each course is laid, put the level on it to make sure it is really level and do not assume that it is if the outside of the brick is upright!

Having brought up the corners to about ten courses, stretch a line along the wall between the two corners and fill in the remainder of the wall to the same height.

Then you start at the corners again, repeating the procedure until your wall reaches the desired height. Frequent checks should be made to see that the work is level – both vertically and horizontally.

Joints will need pointing at intervals; it's impossible to do this as you go along. On houses, pointing often amounts to a skilled job but for farm buildings it's not necessary to take so much trouble.

If the joints are filled in with a small trowel level with the brickwork and, when dried off to some extent, a sack is lightly brushed over to remove any particles adhering to the face of the bricks, a nice-looking job will result.

LAYING CONCRETE BLOCKS

Building in concrete blocks follows much the same technique for bricks.

One of the great advantages of building with blocks is that the work 'rises' much quicker, as the blocks are larger than bricks. Also the work does not use as much mortar.

The general method is the same as for bricks. Provided the first course is set out carefully and a stretcher bonding is followed, the work will go ahead quite quickly.

Blocks make an attractive building if the joints are pointed as recommended for brickwork.

If cavity walls are required, concrete blocks with the cavity made in them have much to commend them, but if plain blocks are used it will be necessary to use metal straps (as in brickwork) to tie the two 'skins' together.

It is usual to leave a 2" cavity, and when four or five courses have been built up on the outside, the inside wall is brought to the same level and the ties are laid across at one-yard intervals (or less). Then the process is repeated.

KEEPING CAVITY CLEAR

Great care must be taken to see that the cavity is kept clean and free from mortar. One way of doing this is to make a straw band with strings at each end for lifting. This is left on one row of ties until the level for the next is reached and the band is then drawn up with any dropped mortar on it.

77

After the next ties have been put in place the band is put on them and so the process starts over again.

It is usual to prop door and window frames in position and to build up to them. When the top of a door frame or window is reached, the lintel – of concrete reinforced with iron rods – is lifted into position and incorporated in the next courses of brick work.

It saves a certain amount of time if care is taken in making the lintels to ensure that they are the right thickness to line up with the brick courses. If you get a lintel of, say, $2\frac{1}{2}$ courses thick, you will have to cut bricks to make it up to three courses to bring the next brick course into line right along the wall.

For details about the construction and fitting of doors and windows see chapter X.

CHAPTER IX

OTHER WAYS OF
BUILDING WALLS

THERE are other ways of building walls than in bricks or concrete blocks. One, of which there are many variants, is to build up the walls layer-by-layer in concrete as it is mixed.

This is a particularly suitable method for small buildings and for framed buildings in which the intervals between the stanchions have to be filled in. It is, perhaps, not so suitable for large buildings not of frame construction. It needs a considerable amount of timber for shuttering, this being made of $1\frac{1}{4}''$ boards planed on one side and both edges (to make close joints) and supported on $2'' \times 4''$ battens.

This shuttering is set up to leave a gap of 6″ to 8″. Great care is necessary to see that it is not only upright but that it is level. The height of the shuttering should not exceed 4′, and the concrete (4 : 2 : 1 mix) must be well worked down as it is filled or it will not be properly consolidated.

When the concrete has set, the shuttering is raised by dismantling and re-erecting higher up for the second 'lift'.

You will probably have to erect platforms to work from, and it is on this second and following 'lifts' that one of the snags of the method of building show up: you have got to lift all the concrete from ground level!

DISADVANTAGES

A highlift loader will lift barrow loads or you must have a hoist. It is the lifting and pouring such weights of concrete that make it a far less satisfactory method of building than with precast concrete blocks. Further, moving the shuttering takes quite a lot of time, and the outlay on the timber is no small item at present prices.

A modification of this method is to use a semi-dry mix of concrete. It requires less shuttering, as immediately one layer is in position the shuttering can be raised for the next layer.

All that is needed is a wooden form made from 1½″ boards long enough to span between two uprights. Rough timber will do if it is faced with flat galvanized sheeting or plywood to present a smooth surface to the concrete.

Strong cross pieces hold the boards together. These are bored to take bolts which, when tightened, hold the form in place on either side of the uprights.

To make the necessary semi-dry mix of concrete, use all-in gravel (size ¾″ down, with 50 per cent sand) with cement and water. With

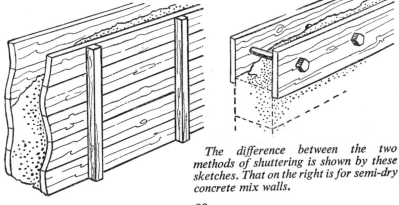

The difference between the two methods of shuttering is shown by these sketches. That on the right is for semi-dry concrete mix walls.

This shows the use of dry-crete blocks for building a boundary wall. Reference to the use of this type of block for farm buildings is on pages 81–82.

ABOVE: *An 8′ × 8′ sliding door built on a 2″ × 1½″ timber frame.*
BELOW: *A round-the-corner door constructed with flat steel sheets on timber frames. Both these photographs were taken on the author's farm.*

moderately dry gravel a mixture of five gallons of water, one cwt cement and seven and a half cubic feet of gravel gives the desired consistency.

While it is difficult to describe the consistency graphically it is necessary to see that it is wet enough to work together without tending to run.

USE SEMI-DRY MIX FOR WALLS

The form is placed in position at the bottom of a pair of uprights and checked for level. Then the mix is put in in 2″ layers, each of which is well hammered down until the top of the form is reached. A block of wood is then placed on top of the concrete and hammered down. The bolts are withdrawn and the form moved up.

This immediate moving up of the form is the reason for the semi-dry mix. With a normal mix it would be necessary to wait for each form full to set before the form could be moved.

The holes left by the bolts are filled with a mixture of sand and cement.

Where windows and doors are required, the wall can be brought up to the sill and recommenced above the opening after a lintel has been placed in position.

This type of concrete wall should be kept damp for ten days or so by spraying with a hose. After that it should be cleaned down and finished off with two coats of cement paint.

WALLS FROM PRECAST PANELS

When walls are to be made of precast panels or sections it will depend upon the type of panel to be used what procedure is to be followed, but in all cases a good foundation is essential, as a considerable amount of weight is to be carried.

In the case of dri-crete the bottom row of blocks are bedded on a ½″ bed of mortar on a good foundation and then the remainder of the courses are simply fitted in dry, care being taken

F

to see that the vertical joints are not immediately above each other but are as in a brick wall.

The base course must, of course, be set perfectly level and true or the wall will not be vertical.

For low boundary walls no more mortar is required until the top coping is placed in position. The top course of blocks – known

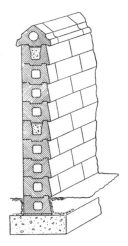

Sketch shows cross-section of boundary wall built with dry-crete blocks. Coping blocks are, of course, not used on walls to carry roofs.

as the band-course – is U shaped; the trough they form is filled with mortar and reinforcing rods are run along in it.

The coping is then placed on and the job is complete.

For higher walls, or those requiring greater strength, a band course of blocks with reinforcement at intervals is used. The suppliers of the blocks will advise on where band-courses are required and on the reinforcing necessary. Both depend upon the actual job to be undertaken.

With this form of building there are special blocks to enable windows to be built in and for partitions to joint into outside walls.

If the walls are to be of corrugated asbestos – flat asbestos is a very unsatisfactory walling for most farm buildings as it is so easily broken – corrugated steel or aluminium, then provision will have to be made to fix it to purlins with hook bolts.

The length of the sheets used will depend upon the height of the wall, but a 9″-overlap should be allowed for at the end of the sheet.

In most positions one corrugation side overlap is sufficient, but if you want to prevent draughts in an unlined building it is probably better to make it two corrugations.

The distance between the purlins will depend partly on the length of the sheet used but 5′ is probably the maximum.

The size of angle iron used for these purlins must depend upon the length of the span between stanchions and upon whether the whole weight of the sheeting is to be carried on them or if the bottom edges of the sheets are to be resting on a dwarf wall.

However, the suppliers of the frame, either steel or concrete, will supply the correct section if you tell them, when ordering, what you propose to clad the walls with.

TO PREVENT ELECTROLYSIS

If aluminium sheets are to be used it must be remembered that if this metal is in contact with iron or steel, electrolysis will take place which will in time – possibly a long time, it depends on the position – eat away the aluminium.

For that reason the special hook bolts etc. should be used and the sheets should be insulated from the steel angle with bitumen felt. When using aluminium sheeting with concrete purlins you have, of course, only to consider the hook bolts in this respect.

CHAPTER X

DOORS AND WINDOWS

MOST people think of doors as always being made of wood, but a simple and neat door for farm buildings can be made with flat steel sheets on a wooden frame. It makes a clean job without any ledges – such as you get on a braced wooden door – and stock cannot chew it! This latter point is very important in the case of pigs and calves.

Once the general idea has been grasped, doors of this kind are far quicker to make than wooden doors and should be far cheaper – unless timber drops very considerably in price.

It naturally depends upon the size of the door what size framing is required and also if the door is to be a sliding one or hinged. The following is a guide:

Size of door	Size of timber for framing
3′ × 3′	1½″ × 1½″
6′ × 3′	2″ × 1½″
6′ × 12′	2″ × 2″
12′ × 12′	2″ × 3″

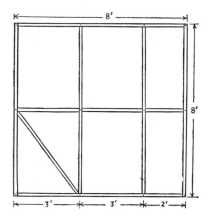

This shows the principle of making a door frame ready for sheeting.

You simply have to make a rectangular frame, brace it with a diagonal member, put blocks where hinges, hangers, locks or bolts have to be attached and, of course, it is necessary to have timber where two sheets join.

Having made the frame then nail on both sides, with galvanized nails, flat galvanized steel sheets; 26 gauge is quite heavy enough.

Where the door is exposed to rain the front sheet should be carried over the top of the door and just lapped over the inside sheet to prevent water getting into the timber at the top of the door. Like this:

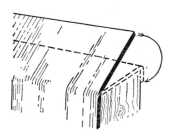

I consider that nearly all doors on the farm should be sliding – except very small ones, such as to calf pens. I have made doors up to $8' \times 8'$ on $2'' \times 1\frac{1}{2}''$ timber. (See photographs facing page 81).

The common objection to the use of sliding doors is that you have to have a bottom channel which is difficult to keep clean. In actual fact this is unnecessary in many cases, as roller guides can be set clear of the doorway and the door simply picks these up as it slides along.

ROUND-THE-CORNER DOORS

It is often a great convenience to have doors sliding round a corner and while this involves making several small doors instead of one large one it is well worth considering. The photograph facing page 81 shows this type of door fitted to a garage, the doors being made of flat steel sheets as mentioned above.

The curve required on the track will be worked out by the makers of the door gear.

There are a number of firms who specialize in making sliding door gear and they are pleased to quote for all the necessary fittings. You simply have to give them the size of the opening, thickness and the probable weight of the door. (Doors made of 26 gauge flat steel sheets on $2'' \times 1\frac{1}{2}''$ framing weigh about 2 lb per square foot.)

Naturally such doors have to be made in narrow sections to be flexible enough to slide round the curve.

The minimum radius usually recommended for the corner curve of the track is $18''$, but generally a $24''$ radius should be used and this is essential when a service door is required, i.e. when the last leaf of the door should open to allow you to enter the building without sliding the door along.

On a $10'$ opening and a $24''$ radius for the track you can have four doors each $2'$ $6''$ wide.

VALUE OF METAL WINDOWS

It is well worth the extra expense in fitting windows to have galvanized steel frames, as the upkeep is so much lower.

There are standard sizes, but for practically all farm buildings a long window is better than a high window. The sill should be set not less than $4'$ $6''$ from the floor. Hopper types are best, as they

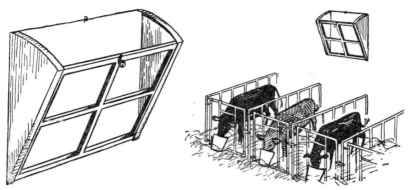

Hopper-type windows give good lighting and ventilation for stock.

provide ventilation when required and cannot be easily damaged when open.

In cowsheds or parlours most of the light is needed on the cows' udders, so the windows should be behind them. A point to remember in siting windows is that a window can be a real nuisance if the light is in your eyes when you are working. You want light behind you, or above you, at all times.

CONSIDER ROOF LIGHTING

The fact that skylights give twice the light for a given area as compared with windows is a great recommendation of this form of lighting. If roofs are made of corrugated asbestos or steel it is simple to insert a sheet of plastic or fibre-glass material. This will be dealt with fully in the next chapter.

There are various types, and some can be obtained in different colours which will reduce glare. Those made of glass fibre help to reduce the amount of heat passed through by the sun's rays and the amount of heat lost from inside the building in cold weather.

The higher roof lights are set in a building the better the light, and the less risk of sunrays falling directly onto the stock.

CHAPTER XI

ROOFING

ROOFING is a branch of building on which many books have been written. Its geometry is a complex subject. But the farmer need not worry too much about that, as he seldom has a complicated roof to deal with and there is no need for him to work out wind pressures, etc.

The slope of a roof is usually expressed in degrees and the actual angle depends upon what material is to be used for cladding.

Thatch is laid on a roof of not less than 45°; tiles are seldom put on a pitch of less than 45° but slates are satisfactory at about 30°, and corrugated steel and asbestos require the lowest pitch of all – about 25°.

CIRCUMSTANCES ALTER CASES

While these figures can be taken as a general rule it must be understood that the situation of a building does to some extent determine what is the best pitch for the purpose, e.g. in a district where heavy snowfalls may be experienced a steeper pitch than normal will be required.

But care should be taken not to exceed a reasonable pitch in the circumstances. If too great a pitch is used, material will be wasted. The simplest type of roof is the lean-to built against an existing building. But its span is very limited or it would have to slope to a great height or be very flat.

For example, with a roof slope of 30° the point of junction with the wall rises from 15' to 20' if the width of the lean-to is increased from 12' to 20'.

FIXING A LEAN-TO ROOF

If a lean-to is to be built against a brick building it is necessary to fix galvanized iron gorbels or make brick gorbels by knocking out bricks and setting new ones into the holes with the ends

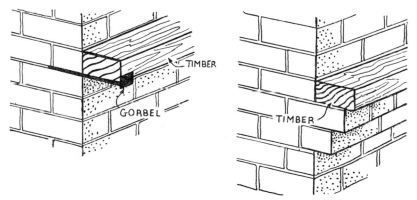

Two methods of fixing a gorbel for a lean-to roof.

projecting. Galvanized iron ones are easy to fix and for a shed up to say 12' wide could be placed at 3' centres.

If the new outside wall is brick, it will be necessary to have a wall-plate on the top of it to carry the roof weight over the entire wall. If the rafters are to carry tiles or slates, they can be at 14" centres.

For full-span buildings, most farmers buy their roof trusses ready made but you can, if you wish, make them from angle iron. If you do, you must appreciate that certain members are under compression and these will have to be increased in size as the span increases. The sizes required for trusses which are to be bolted together with ½″ bolts are shown below.

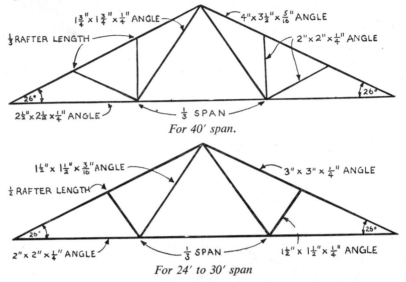

For 40' span.

For 24' to 30' span

It will be noted that the purlins come immediately above the strut. The gusset plates are all made from ¼″ plate. Struts are kept as short as possible; it is for this reason that the tie members are often cambered.

If timber is to be used for roof structures of a span of not more than about 15′ then a collar roof has much to commend it.

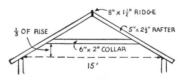

RANGE OF MATERIALS

A wide range of materials is available for roofing. There are three forms of corrugated sheeting – asbestos, galvanized steel or aluminium; there are slates, tiles, shingles and, for small buildings only, tongued and grooved boards covered with tarred felt.

Most farm buildings today are roofed with one of the three corrugated sheetings mentioned.

Of these, corrugated asbestos is the heaviest. It weighs about $3\frac{1}{2}$ lb per square foot with large corrugations and $3\frac{1}{4}$ lb per square foot with small corrugations.

This heavier weight means that heavier and stronger purlins are required and more labour is involved in getting the sheets into position. Against that, asbestos has the advantage that it will not rust and only needs painting for appearances. Further, it is less subject to condensation than metal. And it gives a certain amount of insulation. It is to some extent fireproof.

SIZES AVAILABLE

The sheets with large corrugations, usually called 'big six', can be obtained in 3' to 10' lengths, $41\frac{1}{2}$" wide. They cover a roof width of $39\frac{1}{2}$" when lapped one corrugation.

Small corrugation sheets have 3" corrugations similar to corrugated steel.

The end lap for either type is 6", but if the roof has a low pitch it may be necessary to lap one and a half corrugations with the smaller corrugation type.

Steel sheeting of 24-gauge weighs only $1\frac{3}{4}$ lb per square foot. It can be obtained with corrugations of 3" to 6", but 3" is most common. The usual width is a nominal 2', but this doesn't take into consideration the half corrugation for the lap – which makes actual width 2' 2".

Length of steel sheeting varies from 5' to 12' and gauge of steel from 18 to 28. The smaller the gauge the thicker the sheet. If you order a ton of 10' × 18-gauge sheets you will get 53; if they were 26-gauge there would be 111.

The most common gauge is 24. But for reasonably long life it would be worth going to 22.

DISADVANTAGE OF STEEL

One snag with galvanized steel is that it is often attacked by sulphur fumes; therefore in or near large industrial areas it is best to use asbestos.

Corrugated aluminium sheets are very light. They reduce the labour involved in erection and require less strong purlins. But for large roofs the material is rather expensive.

If aluminium sheeting touches steel, electrolysis will take place which will destroy the fixing or the sheets. The way to prevent this is to use the special hook bolts, etc. which are supplied for the purpose and, where sheets would touch the steel purlins, put an insulation of bitumen felt.

METHODS OF FIXING SHEETS

For fixing corrugated sheets to steel or concrete purlins special hook bolts are used with bituminous fibre washers to prevent water working down the holes. Use a drill to make the holes – not a hammer and nail, particularly with asbestos.

For fixing corrugated sheeting to timber it is necessary to use spring-headed nails – which do not require washers – or roofing screw nails each of which has a galvanized washer and a bituminous fibre washer to prevent water working down the nail hole.

Whether sheeting is fixed by hook bolts or by nails the fixing must always be put through the tops of the corrugations. This is an obvious statement, but I have seen a roof with nails in the valleys – the result being that water came down every nail hole.

When fixing corrugated asbestos sheets it is necessary to mitre overlapping corners as shown in this sketch. The mitre-joint will

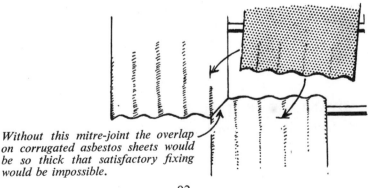

Without this mitre-joint the overlap on corrugated asbestos sheets would be so thick that satisfactory fixing would be impossible.

92

Fittings for Roof Sheeting

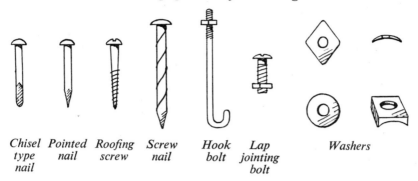

| Chisel type nail | Pointed nail | Roofing screw | Screw nail | Hook bolt | Lap jointing bolt | Washers |

be covered by the fourth sheet when it is put into position. (This is unnecessary with steel or aluminium, as the thickness of each sheet is not so great.)

Side laps are secured by galvanized nuts and bolts, usually $\frac{1}{4}''$ diameter and of suitable length.

CUTTING ROOFING SHEETS

Cutting corrugated sheets is not too easy. Asbestos is best cut with a sheet hack or hand saw and steel with a sheet hack. Alternatively steel can be placed on a piece of timber and cut with a cold chisel and hammer.

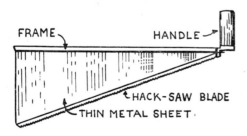

FRAME HANDLE
HACK-SAW BLADE
THIN METAL SHEET

A sheet-hack for cutting corrugated sheets.

The easiest way of all is to use an electric hand saw fitted with an abrasive disc. Suitable discs can be obtained for cutting either asbestos or steel.

Simple roof lighting can be readily inserted during the course

93

of roofing with any of the corrugated sheetings. It is a matter of using an appropriate number of plastic or fibreglass corrugated sheets and putting them in place of the ordinary sheeting in the most suitable position.

Of the two types, fibreglass is slightly cheaper.

These sheets can be bought in all lengths to match with the corrugations of the material being used. Fixing holes can be readily drilled, although the plastic type can be very quickly holed with a small hot soldering iron.

Lights fixed in this way cannot, of course, be opened. Where opening lights are required, frames of asbestos, steel or aluminium should be purchased – with corrugations to match the roofing – and these can subsequently be glazed with glass or plastic sheeting.

BUILDING A CURVED ROOF

Where a curved roof is being applied to reduce trusses to a minimum and allow plenty of head room the method of assembly and fixing is usually to bolt the first row of sheets together while resting on the ground on their edges and then raise them into position. After this the next sheets can be attached to the first 'arch' without difficulty.

If the size of building prevents this method being used, then a platform will probably have to be erected to enable sheets to be put into position before bolting the first arch together; subsequent procedure will then be the same as above.

Curved sheets can be obtained in any of the three materials, and to any radii. Fixed roof lighting or opening lights can be arranged in exactly the same way as previously described, but do make sure that the curve of the lights and the size of corrugation is exactly the same as the other material.

ROOFING IN SLATES

When repairing old roofs or extending an existing building it is often necessary to roof with tiles or slates. There are many types

This shows the principle of centre-nailing for slates.

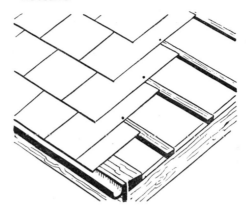

and sizes of tiles and slates but the general principle of fixing them is much the same.

Slates can be laid in two ways – either head nailed, i.e. with nails through holes punched one inch from the top of each slate, or centre nailed – in which case the nails are almost central.

Any advantage lies with centre nailing; with this form of fixing the wind cannot get such leverage under the slate as with head nailing.

As with corrugated sheeting, slates are laid bottom row first and from left to right, or right to left, according to the prevailing wind.

The fascia board has to be raised to tilt the first row of slates. Alternatively, a shaped tile batten can be fixed. Subsequent

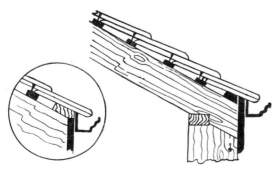

The raised facia board tilts the first row of slates so that subsequent rows lie at the same angle. inset: the same effect can be achieved by using a shaped batten.

95

battens are then nailed to the rafters so that there is an overlap of 3″ on each row of slates.

To find the distance between the centre of battens, take the length of a slate, less the overlap plus 1″ for nailing and divide by two.

Thus, if the slates are 20″ the sum will be $\dfrac{20 - (3+1)}{2}$ – giving 8″ between the battens.

For centre nailing the 1″ does not come into the calculation. The sum here is $\dfrac{20 - 3}{2}$. This gives an answer of $8\frac{1}{2}$″ – the distance between the battens.

Slates are nailed with composition or copper nails. The latter are expensive, but do not use wire nails as they will rust, with the result that sooner or later the slates will start to slip out. Reslating the whole roof is the only answer to that trouble.

Ridges to slated roofs are fixed with mortar and consist of plain angle tiles or capped tiles. When roofing with slates it is worth enquiring at merchants for 'seconds'; alternatively you may find a merchant with sizes which are not stock sizes but which will cost less and make for a cheaper roof. The only difference is that you will have to set the battens to suit the particular size of slate.

ROOFING IN TILES AND SHINGLES

If tiles are to be used it is worth planning the size of a roof, to avoid cutting the tiles if possible.

Pantiles are common in many parts of the country but they should not be used without the roof being first underlined with boarding or with felt. Otherwise, particularly in an open shed, the wind may easily get under the roof and strip the tiles off.

Pantiles also have the disadvantage that, for most of the area of the roof, they are only one tile thick whereas plain tiles are two thicknesses and so reduce the risk of rain penetrating through.

Cedarwood shingles have much to recommend them for farm buildings. When they have weathered they become a silver grey

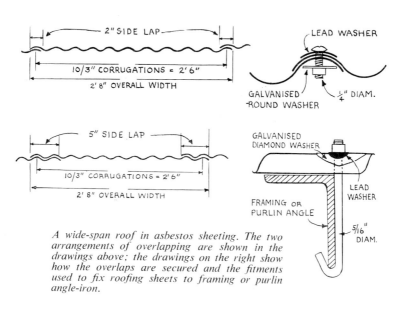

A wide-span roof in asbestos sheeting. The two arrangements of overlapping are shown in the drawings above; the drawings on the right show how the overlaps are secured and the fitments used to fix roofing sheets to framing or purlin angle-iron.

ABOVE AND LEFT: *One of the new corrugated fibre-glass sheetings available for roof lighting. Its strength is shown by the picture on the left.*

Ideal lighting conditions, even in bad weather, can be achieved by the use of proper wall and roof lighting. The building on the right is an excellent example of what can be done.

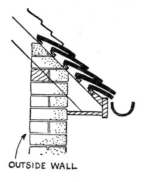

*Method of fixing
pantiles to roof.*

OUTSIDE WALL

which will tone with any landscape. They are light and easily fixed and are very resistant to stripping by wind.

Shingles can be purchased in random widths but the bundles are all the same length.

They should be laid on 3″ × 1″ board spaced 5″ apart. 16″ shingles, for example, should be laid so as to expose 5″ of their length. If they are nailed 1″ above the exposed 5″ line this means that there will be three thicknesses over the entire roof.

Where an old building with rather weak timbers has to be re-roofed there is much to recommend shingles.

ROOFING IN BOARDS AND FELT

Despite the popularity of the boarded and felt-covered roof for small buildings such as poultry houses, I do think that with the high cost of timber and the comparatively short life of this form of roofing it is not by any means a cheap method in the long run.

But it does make a warm windproof roof and has that to commend it. Where it is used, the extra cost of applying the felt to the boards immediately after they have been painted with hot tar is worth while. Felt which is held by light battens only is more likely to yield earlier to the elements.

CHAPTER XII

VENTILATION AND
INSULATION

I T is difficult, if not impossible, to lay down hard and fast rules about ventilation to farm buildings in which stock are to be housed.

Ventilation is very closely tied up with insulation; the two have to be considered together. The aim must be to plan them so that the air in a building can be kept reasonably dry and fresh and as nearly as possible at the best temperature for the stock.

It will help to show how important all this is if, for a moment, we examine what happens during the circulation of air through a building containing stock.

MOIST AIR MUST BE REMOVED

As an animal breathes it draws into its lungs comparatively cool dry air. The temperature is increased through entering the body, and as air temperature increases so does its ability to carry moisture.

Thus, when the air is breathed out it is both warmer and wetter than before it was taken in.

Being warm it rises towards the ceiling of the building and its place is taken by cooler air. If a building had no inlet or outlet, the same air would circulate up and down continuously; indeed it would become so fully saturated that, when inhaled by stock, it would be unable to remove moisture from the lungs. Such conditions are, obviously, unhealthy.

PROPER CONTROL IS ESSENTIAL

But when a building has inlet and outlet ventilation, cool air is drawn in from outside to replace the warm air which escapes.

If the warm air rises against a cool inside roof surface, then proper air circulation is impeded because it will be cooled before it has a chance to leave the building and will deposit its moisture on the inside of the roof and fall to the floor.

On the other hand if warm air strikes a roof surface which is insulated from external atmosphere and is consequently warmer, then it will neither cool nor deposit its moisture content; it will continue rising and disperse through the ventilation outlets.

So, the secret of successful ventilation depends on proper control of inlet of fresh air and outlet of used air together with proper insulation of walls and roofs from external temperature influences.

Let us first deal with the control of ventilation.

INLET VENTILATION

It was at one time thought that the ideal method of ventilation was to have inlet pipes close to the ground and outlets in the roof. But it has now been proved beyond doubt that equally good results can be obtained with inlets at the eaves, particularly if the cold air is deflected upwards.

If the total area of the inlets is slightly smaller than the total area of outlets, there is little risk of air movement getting into reverse but this can happen if the area of inlets far exceeds the area of outlets; in such a case the air can move down from the ridge to the eaves – which is undesirable.

Please turn to page 101

Ventilation

The Old Way

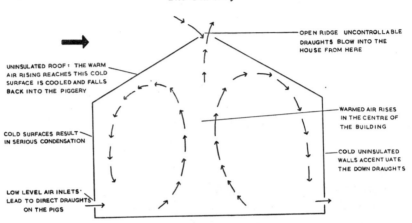

OPEN RIDGE UNCONTROLLABLE DRAUGHTS BLOW INTO THE HOUSE FROM HERE

UNINSULATED ROOF : THE WARM AIR RISING REACHES THIS COLD SURFACE IS COOLED AND FALLS BACK INTO THE PIGGERY

WARMED AIR RISES IN THE CENTRE OF THE BUILDING

COLD SURFACES RESULT IN SERIOUS CONDENSATION

COLD UNINSULATED WALLS ACCENTUATE THE DOWN DRAUGHTS

LOW LEVEL AIR INLETS· LEAD TO DIRECT DRAUGHTS ON THE PIGS

The New Way

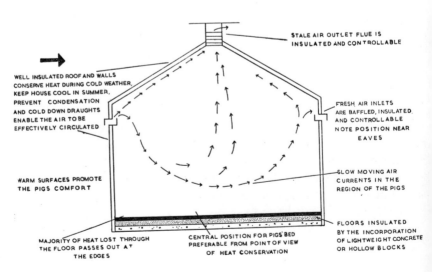

STALE AIR OUTLET FLUE IS INSULATED AND CONTROLLABLE

WELL INSULATED ROOF AND WALLS CONSERVE HEAT DURING COLD WEATHER, KEEP HOUSE COOL IN SUMMER, PREVENT CONDENSATION AND COLD DOWN DRAUGHTS ENABLE THE AIR TO BE EFFECTIVELY CIRCULATED

FRESH AIR INLETS ARE BAFFLED, INSULATED, AND CONTROLLABLE NOTE POSITION NEAR EAVES

WARM SURFACES PROMOTE THE PIGS COMFORT

SLOW MOVING AIR CURRENTS IN THE REGION OF THE PIGS

FLOORS INSULATED BY THE INCORPORATION OF LIGHTWEIGHT CONCRETE OR HOLLOW BLOCKS

MAJORITY OF HEAT LOST THROUGH THE FLOOR PASSES OUT AT THE EDGES

CENTRAL POSITION FOR PIGS' BED PREFERABLE FROM POINT OF VIEW OF HEAT CONSERVATION

100

The drawing opposite shows the ideal movement of air where the outlet can be in the ridge of the roof.

Where there is a ceiling or flat roof the same principles apply: thus, as a general rule I think the needs of stock are best met today

Three ways of achieving inlet ventilation. The baffle in each case is particularly suitable when the inlet has to be low down in the wall.

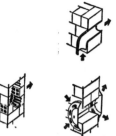

by having inlet ventilators – either grids or drain pipe bends – as near to the eaves as possible. A good plan is to build them into the last-but-one course of bricks.

METHODS OF OUTLET VENTILATION

Raised ridge tiles are often recommended for outlet ventilation, but I think the cowl type of ventilator is the best. It is not affected by direction of wind.

As regards the amount of ventilation, the National Veterinary Medical Association recommends a minimum of 2·6 square inches fixed ventilation inlet area per bacon pig. For cows the Association advises one inlet area of 12 to 18 square inches per two cows.

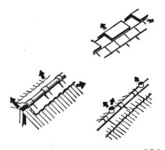

Three ways of achieving outlet ventilation. These are simple but cannot be controlled and are affected by weather.

To cater for summer conditions, when every breath of fresh air is wanted, windows of the hopper type are excellent.

The problem of ventilation and condensation is particularly important with pigs.

TACKLING PIGGERY VENTILATION

A pig gives off something like one and a half cubic feet of carbon dioxide every hour. This, together with the moisture extracted from the lungs and given off by dung and urine, has to be removed without creating draughts or reducing temperature unduly.

Pig houses which are constructed so that the pigs dung and urinate outside do not require so much ventilation as the large Danish-type houses. Even so the baffled door is often not allowing sufficient air to enter.

Again the solution is, in my opinion, the provision of air inlets in the eaves at the front of the house. Air drawn in through the inlets will move up the roof to the outlets; it will dry off a lot of condensation – provided the roof is insulated – and will carry away the carbon dioxide and water vapour that has been exhaled.

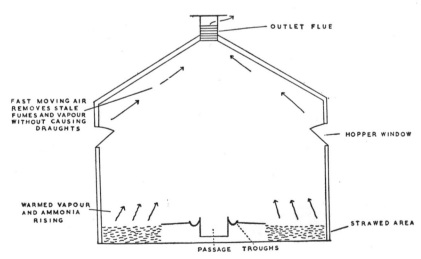

Hopper windows can provide good method of ventilation.

102

For the larger type of pig house where pigs are inside all the time, far greater ventilation is required.

ELECTRIC FANS

Where ventilation is unsatisfactory in old buildings it may be cheaper – rather than make extensive alterations to the walls and roof – to install electric fans.

The following table gives an idea of the size of fan required according to the number of stock, but manufacturers should be consulted on the most suitable type of fan and about the position in which it should be installed. This is a matter for a technical expert.

Size of fan	Revolutions per minute	Approximate number of animals served
12″	1,500	10 cows, 60 pigs, 1,500 poultry
16″	1,200	20 cows, 120 pigs
24″	900	60 cows

Where inlets are required in the walls rather than at the eaves they should be baffled inside to prevent down-draughts on the animals. It is a good plan, in the case of a cavity wall building, to have the ventilation inlet on the inner wall a little higher than on the outer wall. In this way an upward direction of air movement is caused.

System of ventilation for narrow-span buildings with flat roofs or ceilings.

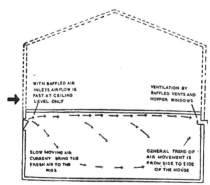

Ventilation outlets should be controllable so that you can increase or decrease the extraction rates according to the number of stock in the building and the outside weather conditions.

PROBLEM OF INSULATION

There are two main types of boards suitable for insulation – insulating board and hardboard.

The former is lightly compressed in manufacture and has a rough surface. If it is required to prevent condensation or absorb sound it should not be plastered.

The latter is made under heavy pressure and is used where a smooth hard surface is required. This is not suitable for taking plaster.

Boards of either kind must be supported at the edges and in the middle when fitted into position, otherwise you will not get a flat wall surface. When fixing insulation boards you need vertical battens at 16" apart for 4' boards and 18" apart for 3' or 6' boards. But if the boards are less than ⅜" thick the vertical battens should be no more than 12" apart.

For hardboards you can put the battens at 15" to 20" apart according to the width of the board and its thickness.

Battens to which the edges of boards are to be fixed should be not less than 2" wide; the others can be 1" wide.

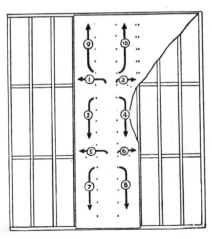

This shows the sequence of nailing or screwing insulating board to battens. It will ensure accurate fitting.

When planning the layout of the battens and when applying the boards, allow for ⅛″ between the edges of each board. This is necessary in case of expansion.

All boards can be cut with a fine-toothed hand saw and should be fixed with rust-proof nails. Where the nail heads are to be covered with plaster use clout nails; but if the heads will not be

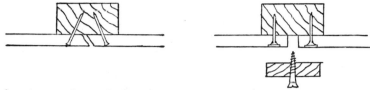

Left: using panel pins. Right: using clout nails which are to be covered by strips or plaster.

hidden then it is best to use panel pins driven in at about 60° in alternate directions. They should be spaced 6″ to 8″ apart.

To make a tidy job the joints require covering, especially if used in a house. If they are covered with strips of metal or special strips of wood, the finish can be very neat and attractive.

A SKILLED JOB

Where the boards are to be plastered, the joints will require strips of wire net or jute scrim before the plastering is started.

Where plastering is necessary, I think it is generally best to employ a skilled man. A farmer wishing to try his hand at it should first get a copy of the Ministry of Works Advisory Leaflet No. 9 (Plaster Mixes) – it costs 3*d*. from H.M. Stationery Office, York House, Kingsway, London, W.C.2 – and study that in detail.

CHAPTER XIII

THE ART OF PLUMBING

FEW jobs on the farm take up so much time as carrying water – be it in buckets, churns or in tanks. Yet at the end there is nothing to see for the labour involved.

Nevertheless water has got to be moved to the point where it is required for use, and a considerable amount of labour can be saved by a piped water supply.

The following table shows the approximate quantities of water required by stock:

Cows	10–20 gallons per cow per day.
Pigs	1–2 gallons per pig per day.
Poultry	About 1 gallon for each 25 birds.
For cows in sheds allow 30–40 gallons per day for all requirements.	
For pigs in houses allow 2–3 gallons per day for all requirements.	

The cost of pipes and fittings is not great, but the labour involved in fitting them up is costly so it well pays to master the few simple details required in this work when it can be done with mild steel pipes – galvanized being the best.

You have not got to be a trained plumber unless you want to extend the scope of the work to lead pipes. Wiping the joints etc. with lead piping does require considerable practice.

The minimum tools required for working in galvanized piping are shown in the sketch here.

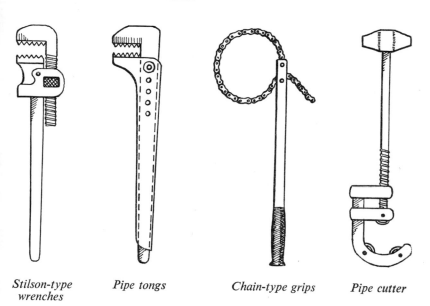

Stilson-type   Pipe tongs   Chain-type grips   Pipe cutter
wrenches

Stilson-type wrenches – with a capacity of $\frac{1}{2}''$ to $4''$ pipes – are adjustable; the medium-size ones are best. The pipe tongs are also adjustable. To have a pair of each is often an advantage; in any case you need two grips of some sort. The chain type are excellent, more especially where pipes have been run close to walls. They do not tend to mark the pipes quite so much.

Pipes can be cut with a hack-saw or with a pipe cutter. The latter is tightened as it revolves round the pipe and the cutters bite into it. These tools ensure a square end to the pipe, but this is not difficult to obtain with a hack-saw.

A pipe vice is essential as it is impossible to hold a pipe in an ordinary engineer's vice without damaging it; and only in a pipe vice is it possible to hold a pipe tight enough to put a thread on the end.

In measuring a pipe before you cut it it is necessary to remember that the ends have to be threaded into fittings; so the pipe is cut longer than it will finally appear on the job. This is made clear below.

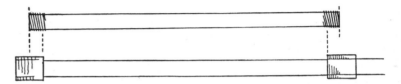

When cutting a pipe length allow for threadings for fittings.

It is necessary to have a set of dies for threading the pipes and these can be bought with a range of sizes to fit the one stock, a ratchet type being the easiest to use.

The other thing to be mastered is the names of the various fittings, as you cannot order your requirements without this. Also remember that the threads on pipes are 'gas thread' – you cannot use Whitworth dies.

The size of a pipe is always taken by its inside diameter. Thus a 1″ nominal bore has an outside diameter of $1\frac{11}{32}$″.

STUDY RANGE OF FITTINGS

If you have not done any pipe work before, it might be worth asking your ironmonger to let you see his stock of fittings as their uses will become more obvious than from an explanation in a book, but it may be helpful to bear the following in mind.

Sockets (or collars as they are sometimes called) normally join two pipes together, and when bends or lengths of pipe are bought they usually have one collar per length.

Bends can be obtained with a male and a female end, in which case the collar is made in it. Where the bend is short, an elbow can be used but square elbows do reduce the flow of water considerably.

Where it is necessary to reduce the size of a pipe, a reducing socket is used – or a reduction bush can take its place.

This is an example of where a little thought should be given to planning the run of the pipes. If you have, say, a 1″ pipe and you want to take a ¾″ branch off it, you can get a tee-piece with 1″ at each end and with a branch ¾″, or a tee with all three openings 1″ and then use a bush with a 1″ outside diameter and ¾″ inside, or again a 1″ nipple could go into the tee and then a 1″ to ¾″ reduction socket.

The first method would require one fitting, the second two, and the third three; so the cost of the job can be increased by the use of unnecessary fittings.

On the other hand, when making alterations to existing pipes it often pays to use extra fittings rather than pull a lot of the old work down.

PLAN THE WORK

When planning the work try to plan it so that you can start from one end and work right through to the other on the main with branches inserted where required. This makes for easy working and the minimum use of connectors.

It will be readily appreciated that when two pipes that have already been fixed have to be joined you cannot screw one onto the other. To overcome this you use a connector with a backnut. The socket is run back until the end of the thread is showing; and then, by putting it against the end of the other pipe, the socket is run onto that thread. Subsequently the backnut is run down after

Sketches show the three steps involved in joining two pipes together by socket and backnut.

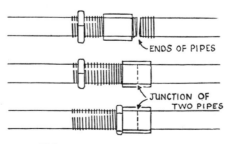

ENDS OF PIPES

JUNCTION OF TWO PIPES

packing round the end of the socket and thus a water-tight joint is made.

Socket unions can be used in some places and then the nut simply has to be screwed onto the flange on the other pipe.

PIPE-FITTING HINTS

When pipes are cut it is necessary to file a slight taper on the end so as to facilitate the start of the die.

Use oil when threading. There are a number of compounds for putting on the thread during the fitting of the pipes and if a little tow or fine thread is used at the same time it makes a really good joint.

Red lead was at one time a common jointing material, but as it is poisonous and makes it difficult to take joints apart there is nothing to recommend it; proprietary jointing compounds are strongly preferred.

Where the farmer is really good at welding he can join pipes by welding but he must have the necessary skill or he will have trouble with leaks.

WATER TANKS

When ordering tanks it is worth having the flanges put in at the required points. If you have to put an additional pipe into a tank it can be done by the use of a flange inside and a backnut outside, packing behind the flange well with jointing compound.

All water systems have to have taps or control valves, so it may be as well to know the names and uses to which they are put.

Stopcocks have to be fitted the correct way round, as it is the pressure of the water coming out of the sediment chamber which lifts the washer.

Stopcocks fitted with disc wheels instead of handles are known as wheel or globe valves. There are also wedge-gate valves which

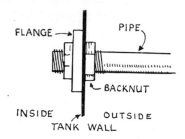

*Method of fitting a pipe
into a tank which has not
got a flange.*

are normally used for larger sizes. The gate is moved vertically to give an unrestricted flow when fully open.

The bib-cock is the common type of tap, having renewable washers. It can be obtained with hose connectors if required. The only other water controls the farm is likely to need are the ball-valves or ball-cocks which are put in cisterns to control the level of the water.

A WORD ABOUT WASHERS

Maintenance of taps and ball-valves is vital if the waste of water is to be avoided. It is said that one drop a minute is two gallons a day. Yet you often see taps dripping at the rate of several drops a second!

To renew the washers in bib-cocks the stuffing box has to be removed. (If the taps are the easy-clean type the cover will have to be taken off, a set screw in the crutch is then removed and the crutch can be knocked off with a piece of wood.)

The plunger, with the washer attached, can be withdrawn after the removal of the stuffing box, and a new washer fitted by the removal of the small nut.

It used to be the rule to fit a leather washer for cold water and a fibre one for hot, but now composite washers are available which can be used for either. This saves stocking two types.

There are high-pressure and low-pressure ball-valves – the difference being that for high-pressure the hole against which the washer presses when the valve is raised is of small diameter.

If you fit a high-pressure ball-valve on a low-pressure system the water will run very slowly into the tank; on the other hand a low-pressure ball-valve on a high-pressure system is likely to leak, as the ball cannot press the washer hard enough to stop the flow of water completely.

WATER PUMPS

Where mains water is not available the question of pumps arises.

There are many types of pumps, and if a complete water system has to be installed on the farm the farmer must decide which is the most suitable for his purposes.

Plunger-type pumps are seldom installed today; the most common types are piston (single- or double-acting) and centrifugal.

The double-acting piston pump is satisfactory where the quantity of water required is not great. The common type has a piston working in a horizontal cylinder with valves on either side so that as one draws water the other pumps it.

This reduces the tendency for thumping in the pipes. A further help to reduce this is to have air vessels; these have a valve in them through which air can be drawn, and the air acts as a cushion to the water.

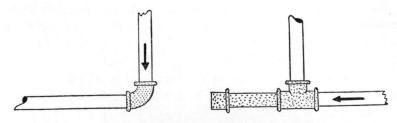

Water in the T-joint acts as a cushion and eliminates thumping.

This thumping, which is known as 'hammering', in the pipes can be serious – as apart from the noise it can damage the joints in the pipes. It can be overcome by inserting a T instead of a bend.

Self-priming centrifugal pumps are limited to about 26′ lift and

112 *Please turn to page 145*

USEFUL
PLANS

of Latest Style Farm Buildings
and Interior Fittings

These include a number of plans
recommended by the Ministry of
Agriculture and are supplemented by
recently-devised layouts prepared
by leading practical farm buildings
architects.

METHODS OF INSULATING FLOORS

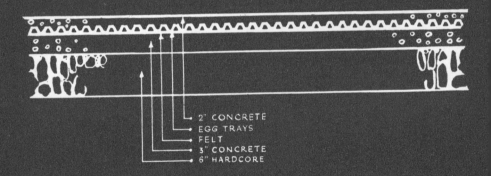

2" CONCRETE
EGG TRAYS
FELT
3" CONCRETE
6" HARDCORE

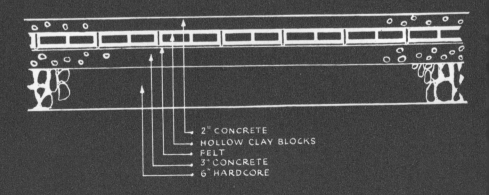

2" CONCRETE
HOLLOW CLAY BLOCKS
FELT
3" CONCRETE
6" HARDCORE

METHOD
OF
INSULATING
ROOFS

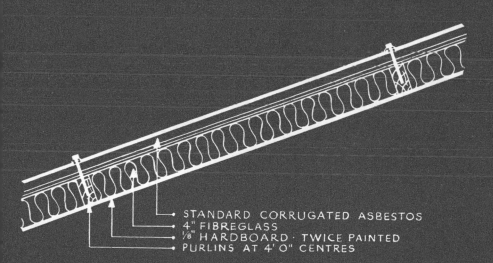

STANDARD CORRUGATED ASBESTOS
4" FIBREGLASS
1/8" HARDBOARD · TWICE PAINTED
PURLINS AT 4' 0" CENTRES

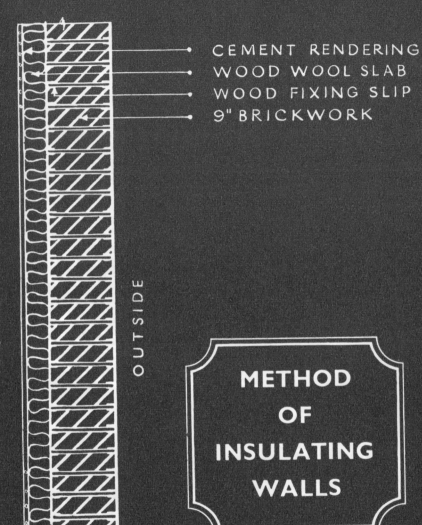

CEMENT RENDERING
WOOD WOOL SLAB
WOOD FIXING SLIP
9" BRICKWORK

INSIDE

OUTSIDE

METHOD

OF

INSULATING

WALLS

TEMPORARY PARTITIONS

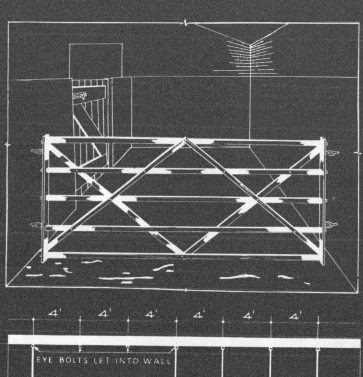

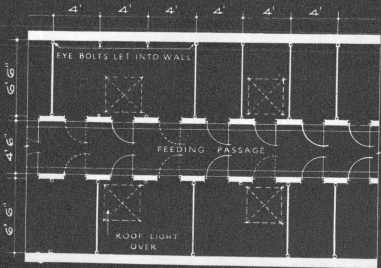

4'　4'　4'　4'　4'　4'

EYE BOLTS LET INTO WALL

6'6"

4'6"

FEEDING PASSAGE

6'6"

ROOF LIGHT
OVER

SINGLE-ROW COWHOUSE

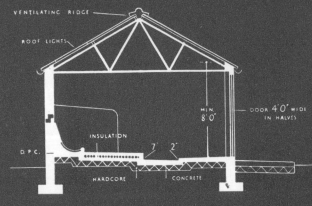

Single-row cowhouse should not have more than twenty standings.

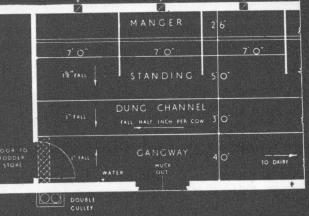

Plan can be extended up to required number of standings.

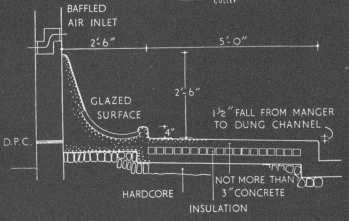

MANGER and STANDING

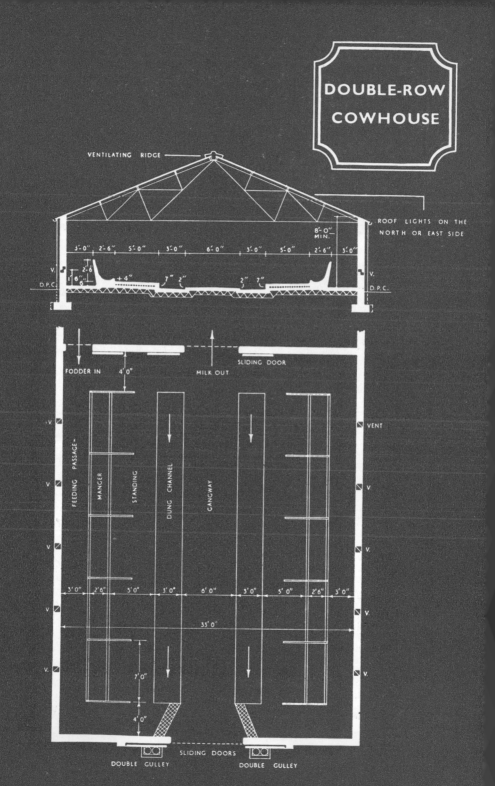

DOUBLE-ROW
COWHOUSE

VENTILATING RIDGE

ROOF LIGHTS ON THE
NORTH OR EAST SIDE

8'-0"
MIN.

3'-0" 2'-6" 5'-0" 3'-0" 6'-0" 3'-0" 5'-0" 2'-6" 3'-0"

V.   V.

2'-6"
1'-6" +4" 7" 2"   2" 7"
D.P.C.   D.P.C.

FODDER IN   4'0"   MILK OUT   SLIDING DOOR

V.   VENT

FEEDING PASSAGE

MANGER

STANDING

DUNG CHANNEL

GANGWAY

V.   V.

V.   V.

3'0" 2'6" 5'0" 3'0" 6'0" 3'0" 5'0" 2'6" 3'0"

V.   V.

35'0"

V.   V.

7'0"

4'0"

SLIDING DOORS

DOUBLE GULLEY   DOUBLE GULLEY

ABREAST-TYPE MILKING PARLOURS

This section and plan do not correspond. The section is of a two-level arrangement, plan is for single-level.

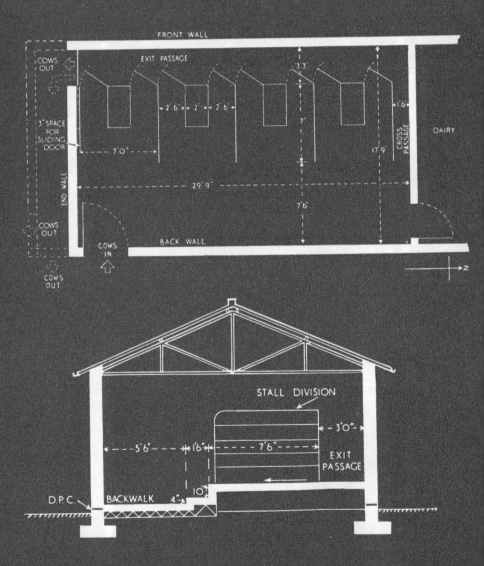

TANDEM-TYPE MILKING PARLOUR

The section on this page deals only with the arrangement of the parlour and does not include the adjacent dairy.

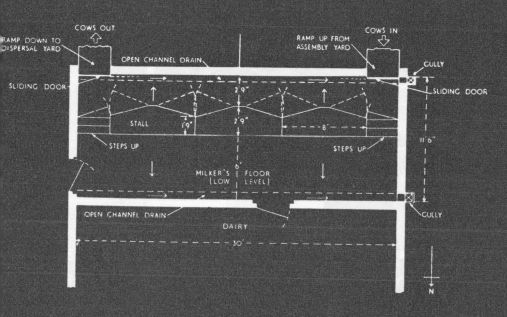

COWS OUT

RAMP DOWN TO DISPERSAL YARD

OPEN CHANNEL DRAIN

RAMP UP FROM ASSEMBLY YARD

COWS IN

GULLY

SLIDING DOOR

2'9"

SLIDING DOOR

STALL

1'9"

2'9"

8'

STEPS UP

STEPS UP

11'6"

MILKER'S FLOOR (LOW LEVEL)

6'

OPEN CHANNEL DRAIN

GULLY

DAIRY

30'

N

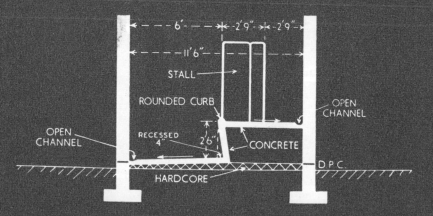

6'

2'9"

2'9"

11'6"

STALL

OPEN CHANNEL

ROUNDED CURB

OPEN CHANNEL

RECESSED 4"

2'6"

CONCRETE

D.P.C.

HARDCORE

YARD AND PARLOUR for 10-20 Cows

The arrangement suggested here allows for herd expansion.

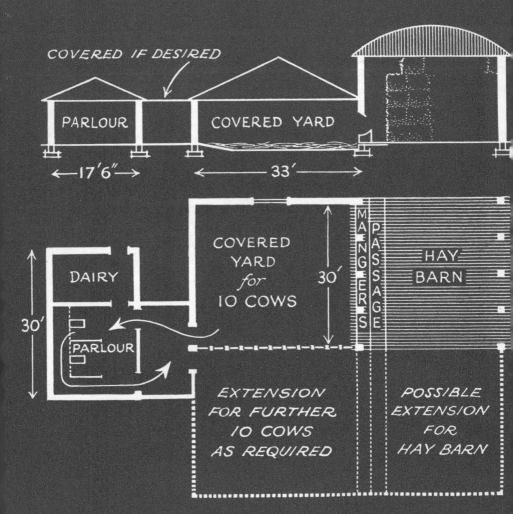

COVERED IF DESIRED

PARLOUR

COVERED YARD

←17'6"→   ←33'→

COVERED YARD *for* 10 COWS

DAIRY

30'

30'

PARLOUR

MANGERS

PASSAGE

HAY BARN

EXTENSION FOR FURTHER 10 COWS AS REQUIRED

POSSIBLE EXTENSION FOR HAY BARN

This layout lends itself to making silage under cover in the barn – possibly for self-feeding.

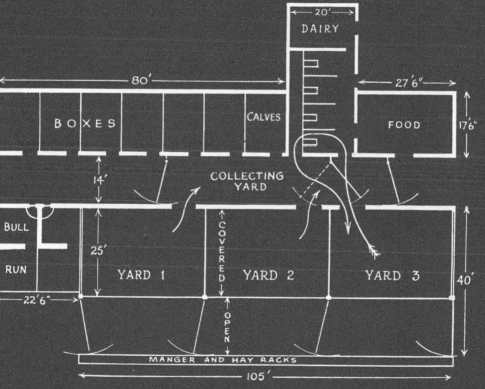

YARD AND PARLOUR for 30-40 Cows

Where it is desired to keep initial costs as low as possible, the yards can be partly covered as shown. In that case the floor of the open part should be kept free of straw.

20′

DAIRY

80′

27′6″

BOXES

CALVES

FOOD

17′6″

14′

COLLECTING YARD

BULL

COVERED

25′

RUN

YARD 1

YARD 2

YARD 3

40′

OPEN

22′6″

MANGER AND HAY RACKS

105′

A dutch barn for silage, hay and straw – adjacent to the racks and mangers in the yard – would complete the layout.

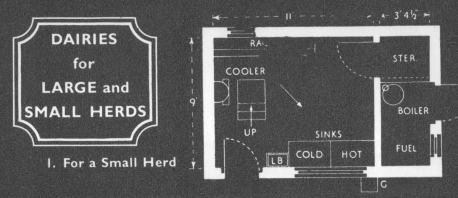

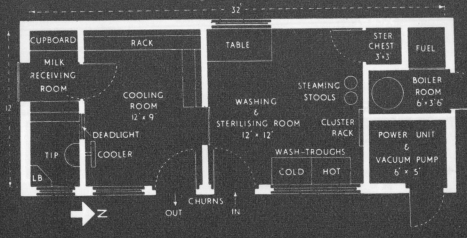

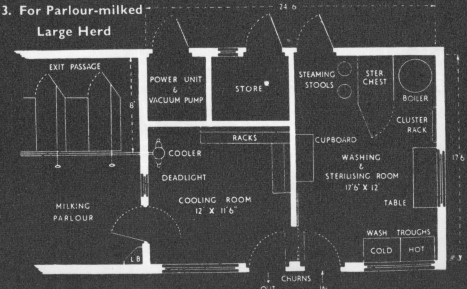

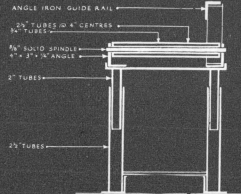

ANGLE IRON GUIDE RAIL

2½" TUBES @ 4" CENTRES
¾" TUBES

⅝" SOLID SPINDLE
4" × 3" × ¼" ANGLE

2" TUBES

2½" TUBES

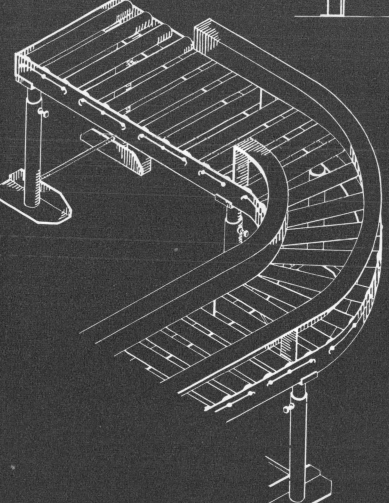

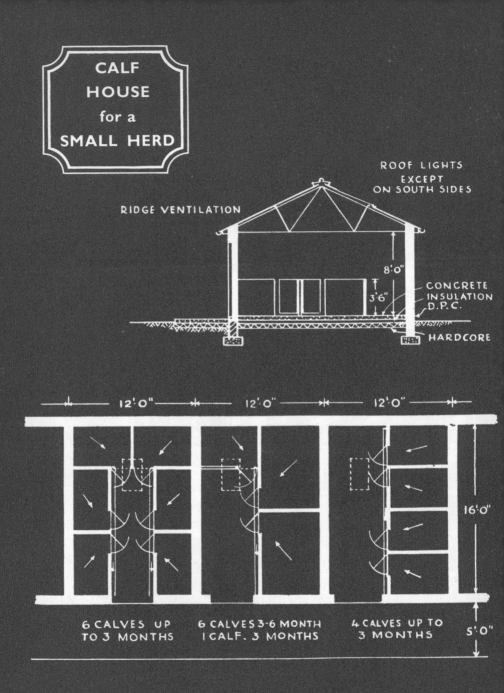

CALF HOUSE for a SMALL HERD

RIDGE VENTILATION

ROOF LIGHTS EXCEPT ON SOUTH SIDES

8'·0"

3'·6"

CONCRETE
INSULATION
D.P.C.

HARDCORE

12'·0" 12'·0" 12'·0"

16'·0"

5'·0"

6 CALVES UP TO 3 MONTHS

6 CALVES 3-6 MONTH 1 CALF. 3 MONTHS

4 CALVES UP TO 3 MONTHS

Three alternative interior layouts are shown. Choose the one most suitable to the needs of the farm.

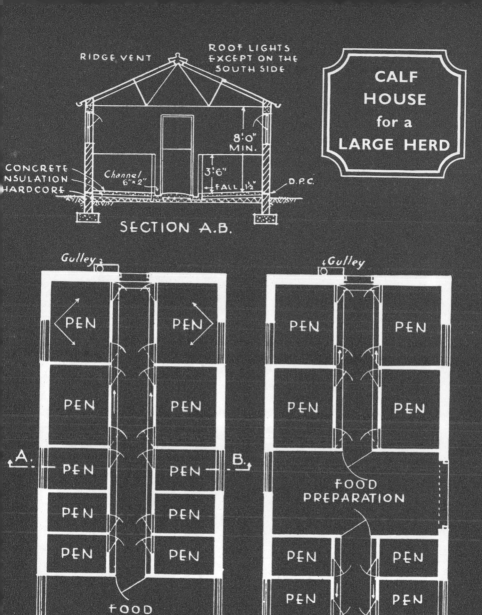

RIDGE VENT

ROOF LIGHTS
EXCEPT ON THE
SOUTH SIDE

8'0" MIN.

3'6"

CONCRETE
INSULATION
HARDCORE

Channel
6"×2"

FALL 1½"

D.P.C.

SECTION A.B.

CALF
HOUSE
for a
LARGE HERD

Gulley

PEN   PEN

PEN   PEN

A.   PEN   PEN   B.

PEN   PEN

PEN   PEN

FOOD
PREPARATION

"A"

Gulley

PEN   PEN

PEN   PEN

FOOD
PREPARATION

PEN   PEN

PEN   PEN

PEN   PEN

Gulley

"B"

PLANS

The only difference between the two alternative plans is the siting of the food preparation
area and the drainage.

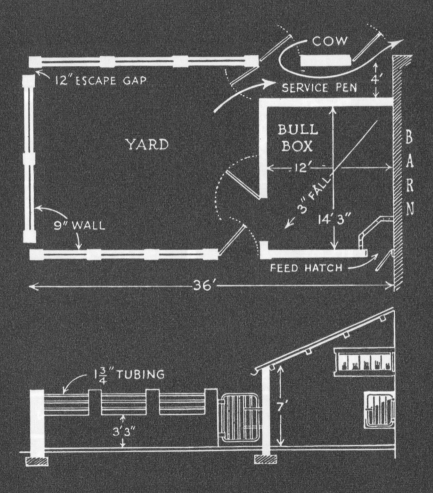

A lean-to type of pen. The bull can be managed (fed and mated) without anyone having to enter the pen.

BULL PEN
No. 2

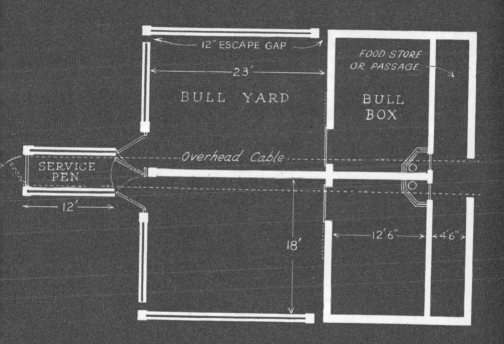

12" ESCAPE GAP

23'

BULL YARD

FOOD STORE
OR PASSAGE

BULL
BOX

Overhead Cable

SERVICE
PEN

12'

18'

12'6"

4'6"

Alternative type of bull-pen layout. One box
and yard can be built first and repeated at a
later date for second bull.

FARROWING AND REARING HOUSE

When used as a fattening house the crate boarding should be removed.

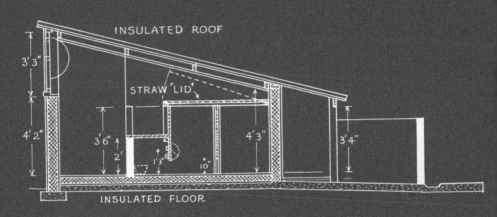

INSULATED ROOF

STRAW "LID"

3' 3"

4' 2"

3' 6"

2'

1' 3"

10"

4' 3"

3' 4"

INSULATED FLOOR

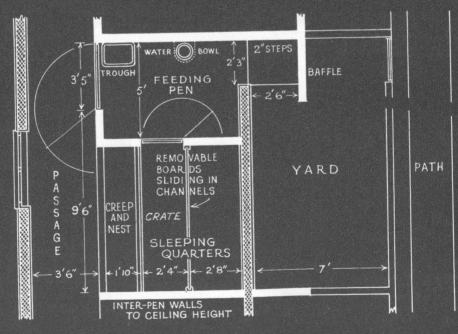

WATER BOWL

2" STEPS

TROUGH

FEEDING PEN

2' 3"

BAFFLE

3' 5"

5'

2' 6"

PASSAGE

9' 6"

REMOVABLE BOARDS SLIDING IN CHANNELS

CRATE

CREEP AND NEST

SLEEPING QUARTERS

YARD

PATH

3' 6"

1' 10"

2' 4"

2' 8"

7'

INTER-PEN WALLS TO CEILING HEIGHT

To carry pigs right through
from birth to bacon.

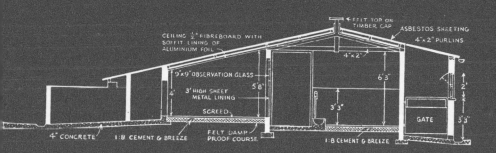

ALL-PURPOSE PIG HOUSE

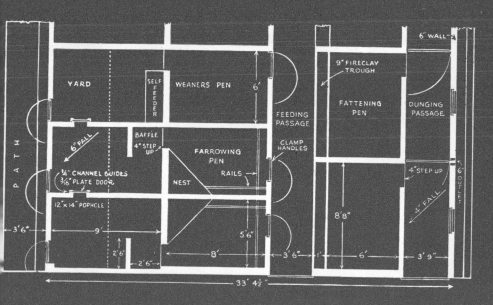

Sows farrow in small pens. Litters can mix at
about 6 weeks, they then go to weaners' pen.
At about 12 weeks they go to the fattening
pens.

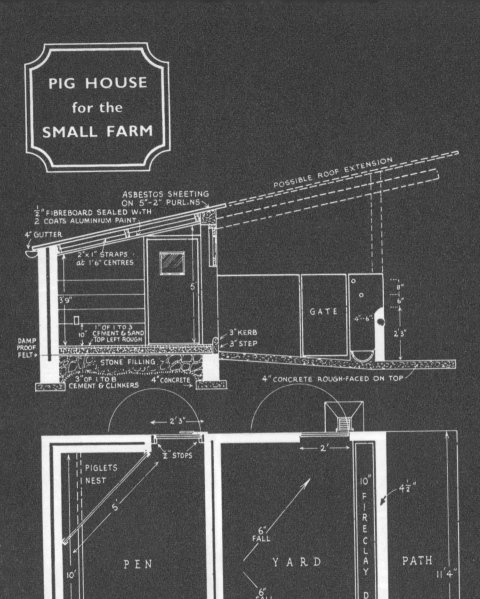

PIG HOUSE for the SMALL FARM

POSSIBLE ROOF EXTENSION

ASBESTOS SHEETING ON 5"–2" PURLINS

½" FIBREBOARD SEALED WITH 2 COATS ALUMINIUM PAINT

4" GUTTER

2"× 1" STRAPS at 1'6" CENTRES

5'

3'9"

1" OF 1 TO 3 CEMENT & SAND TOP LEFT ROUGH

10"

DAMP PROOF FELT →

STONE FILLING

3" OF 1 TO 8 CEMENT & CLINKERS

4" CONCRETE

3" KERB
3" STEP

GATE

1"
8"
6"
4"...6"

2'3"

4" CONCRETE ROUGH-FACED ON TOP

2'3"

2" STOPS

PIGLETS NEST

5'

10'

PEN

6'

6"
FALL

6"
FALL

YARD

5'6"

10"
FIRECLAY DISH

2'

4½"

PATH

11'4"

3'

6" GRATING TO DRAIN

4" OUTLET

7'4"

WALLS: 2 LEAVES OF 3" CONCRETE BLOCKS OR BRICK ON EDGE WITH CROSS TIES EVERY 2'

132

PIG
FEEDING
TROUGH

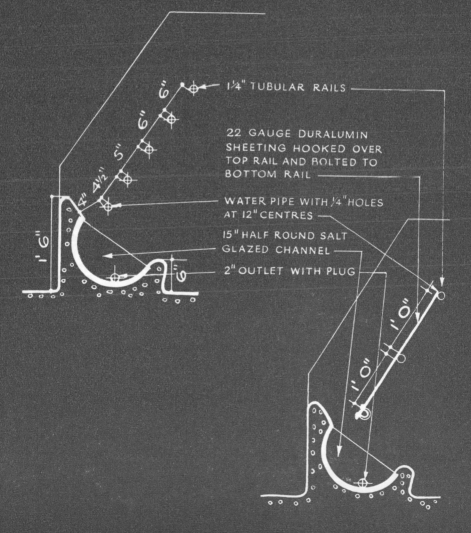

1¼" TUBULAR RAILS

22 GAUGE DURALUMIN
SHEETING HOOKED OVER
TOP RAIL AND BOLTED TO
BOTTOM RAIL

WATER PIPE WITH ¼" HOLES
AT 12" CENTRES

15" HALF ROUND SALT
GLAZED CHANNEL

2" OUTLET WITH PLUG

6"

6"

6"

5"

4½"

4"

1' 6"

6"

1' 0"

1' 0"

1' 0"

LIQUID MANURE INSTALLATION

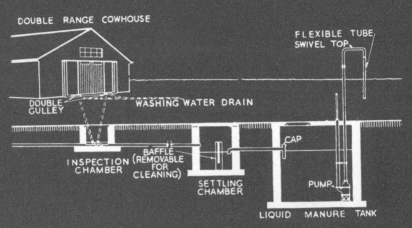

DOUBLE RANGE COWHOUSE

FLEXIBLE TUBE SWIVEL TOP

DOUBLE GULLEY

WASHING WATER DRAIN

INSPECTION CHAMBER

BAFFLE (REMOVABLE FOR CLEANING)

SETTLING CHAMBER

CAP

PUMP.

LIQUID MANURE TANK

SECTIONAL VIEW OF INSTALLATION

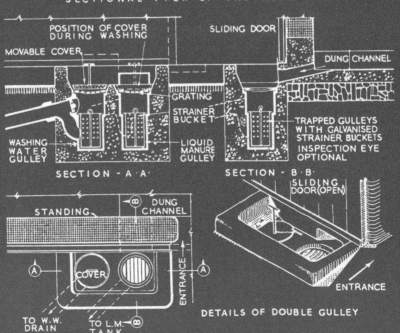

POSITION OF COVER DURING WASHING

MOVABLE COVER

SLIDING DOOR

DUNG CHANNEL

GRATING

STRAINER BUCKET

WASHING WATER GULLEY

LIQUID MANURE GULLEY

TRAPPED GULLEYS WITH GALVANISED STRAINER BUCKETS
INSPECTION EYE OPTIONAL

SECTION - A·A·

SECTION - B·B·

SLIDING DOOR (OPEN)

STANDING

DUNG CHANNEL

COVER

ENTRANCE

TO W.W. DRAIN

TO L.M. TANK.

ENTRANCE

DETAILS OF DOUBLE GULLEY

134

DEEP-LITTER POULTRY HOUSE
for 300 birds

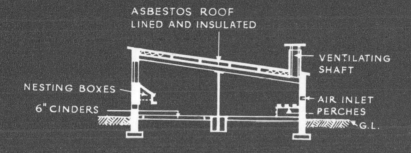

ASBESTOS ROOF
LINED AND INSULATED

VENTILATING
SHAFT

NESTING BOXES

6" CINDERS

AIR INLET
PERCHES

G.L.

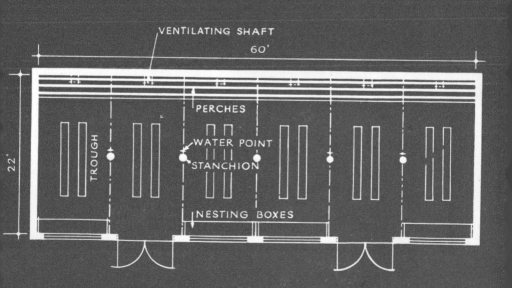

VENTILATING SHAFT

60'

PERCHES

WATER POINT

TROUGH

STANCHION

22'

NESTING BOXES

SHEEP-DIPPING BATH

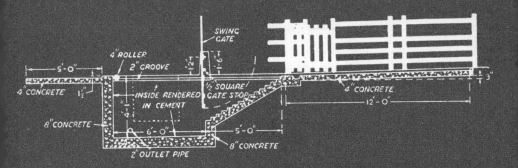

SWING GATE

4" ROLLER
2" GROOVE

5'-0"

4" CONCRETE
1½"

INSIDE RENDERED IN CEMENT

½ SQUARE GATE STOP

½ SQUARE GATE STOP

4" CONCRETE

3"

8" CONCRETE

6'-0"

5'-0"

12'-0"

2" OUTLET PIPE

8" CONCRETE

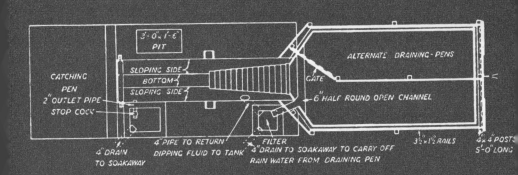

3'-0" × 1'-6" PIT

ALTERNATE DRAINING-PENS

CATCHING PEN

SLOPING SIDE
BOTTOM
SLOPING SIDE

GATE

2" OUTLET PIPE
STOP COCK

6" HALF ROUND OPEN CHANNEL

FILTER

4" DRAIN TO SOAKAWAY

4" PIPE TO RETURN DIPPING FLUID TO TANK

4" DRAIN TO SOAKAWAY TO CARRY OFF RAIN WATER FROM DRAINING PEN

3½" × 1½" RAILS

4 × 4" POSTS 5'-0" LONG

SHEEP-DIPPING
BATH
(Detail)

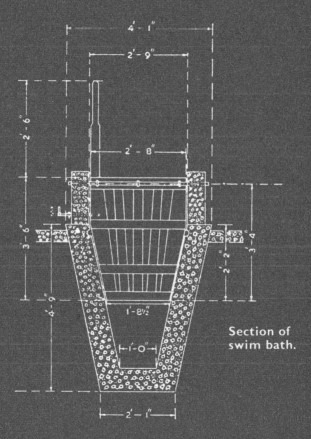

Section of
swim bath.

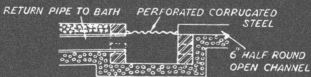

RETURN PIPE TO BATH   PERFORATED CORRUGATED
STEEL

6" HALF ROUND
OPEN CHANNEL

Section through filter.

137

LAYOUT OF
TYPICAL
GRAIN STORE

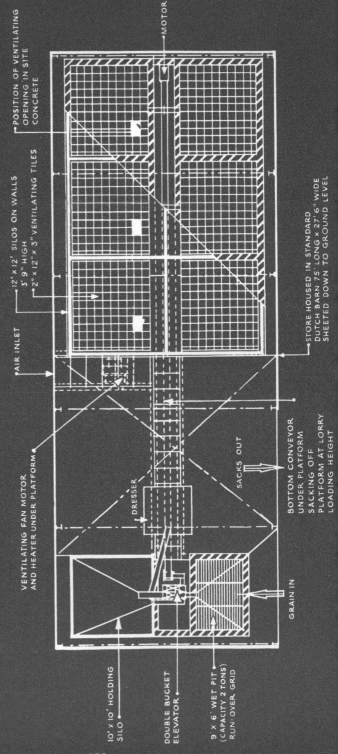

POSITION OF VENTILATING OPENING IN SITE CONCRETE

MOTOR

12' x 12' SILOS ON WALLS 3' 9" HIGH

2" x 12" x 3" VENTILATING TILES

AIR INLET

STORE HOUSED IN STANDARD DUTCH BARN 75' LONG x 27' 6" WIDE SHEETED DOWN TO GROUND LEVEL

VENTILATING FAN MOTOR AND HEATER UNDER PLATFORM

DRESSER

BOTTOM CONVEYOR UNDER PLATFORM SACKING OFF PLATFORM AT LORRY LOADING HEIGHT

SACKS OUT

GRAIN IN

10' x 10' HOLDING SILO

DOUBLE BUCKET ELEVATOR

9' x 6' WET PIT (CAPACITY 2 TONS) RUN-OVER GRID

138

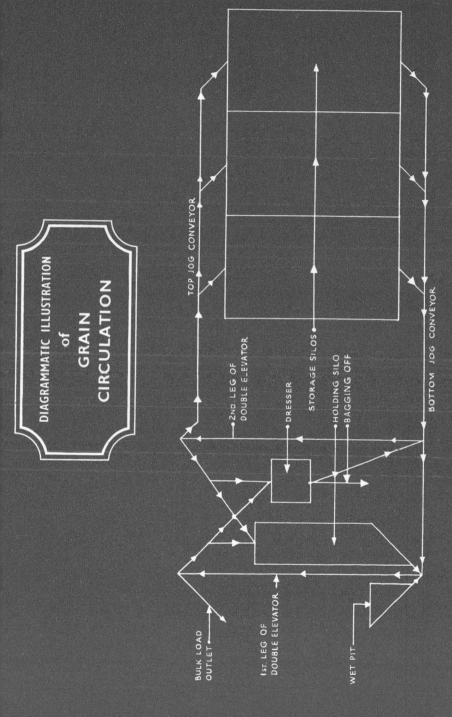

DIAGRAMMATIC ILLUSTRATION
of
GRAIN
CIRCULATION

TOP JOG CONVEYOR

2ND. LEG OF DOUBLE ELEVATOR

DRESSER

STORAGE SILOS

HOLDING SILO

BAGGING OFF

BOTTOM JOG CONVEYOR

BULK LOAD OUTLET

1ST. LEG OF DOUBLE ELEVATOR

WET PIT

Isometric Sketch
of
GRAIN STORE
VENTILATING DUCTS

12" × 12" × 3" VENTILATING TILES ON 6" × 6" × 9" HIGH
PRECAST CONCRETE PIERS

PRECAST SILOS

GRAIN OUTLET FROM SILOS

CONCRETE FILLET SLOPING AT AN
ANGLE OF 45°

9" CONCRETE SLAB

REINFORCEMENT

10" REINFORCED
CONCRETE RAFT

VENTILATING
OPENING

SLIDING VALVE

VENTILATING DUCT

9" REINFORCED CONC

9" BRICKWORK (OR R. CONCRETE)

SHAKER CONVEYOR

IMPLEMENT
SHED

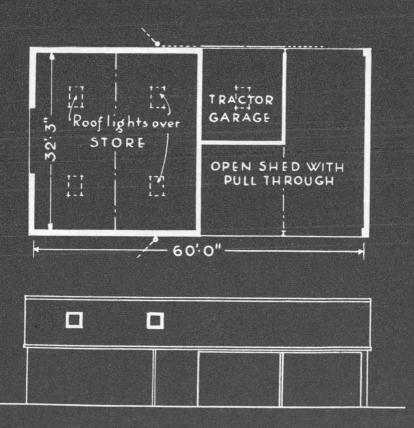

Roof lights over
STORE

32' 3"

TRACTOR
GARAGE

OPEN SHED WITH
PULL THROUGH

60' 0"

CATTLE GRID

Sleeper on edge

	5″	3″ Iron cart tyre fixed
	5″	with 2″ coach screws
2″ O.D. Tube	5″	
	5″	
	5″	
	5″	2×2 Angle →
	5″	
	4″	
	5″	
	5″	1½″ × ¼″ Holding down strip
	5″	
	5″	
	5″	
	5″	

8′6″   9′4″

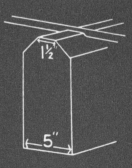

1½

5″

Sleeper

CATTLE CRUSH

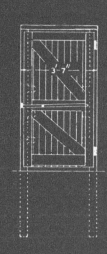

3'-7"

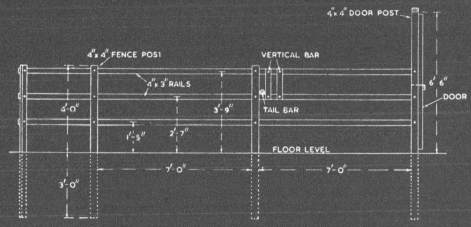

4"x 4" DOOR POST

4"x 4" FENCE POST

VERTICAL BAR

4"x 3" RAILS

6' 6"

4'-0"

3'-9"

TAIL BAR

DOOR

1'-5"

2'-7"

FLOOR LEVEL

7'-0"

7'-0"

3'-0"

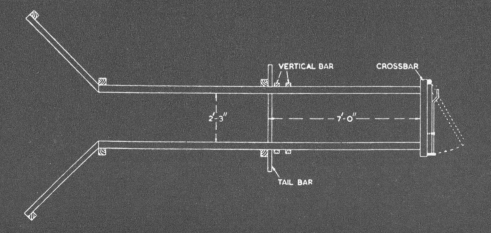

VERTICAL BAR

CROSSBAR

2'-3"

7'-0"

TAIL BAR

WORKSHOP

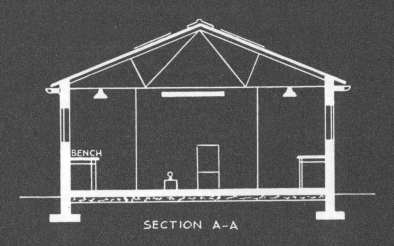

BENCH

SECTION A-A

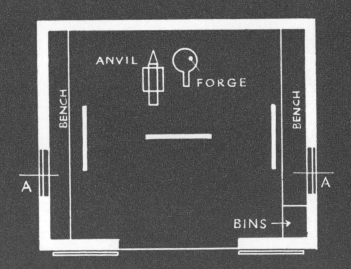

ANVIL

FORGE

BENCH

BENCH

A

A

BINS →

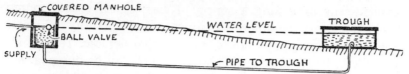

Useful way of preventing pipes to field trough from freezing.

are suitable for being driven by electric motor, as they can be fixed direct onto the shaft of the motor.

The submersible pumps are centrifugal and give excellent service. They have the advantage that everything is under water and so the risk of damage by flooding is nil.

Electricity is the most satisfactory way of running a pump, as it can be made quite automatic. If the water is pumped into a tank from which it gravitates to the taps, then a float switch can be fitted to cut out the motor as soon as the tank fills and to start the motor again when the water falls to a predetermined level.

PRESSURE TANK SYSTEM

To my mind the most satisfactory type of water system is the pressure tank system. In this, the water is pumped into a closed tank. As the air is compressed by the water so a pressure is built up.

When the pressure reaches a predetermined point – say 40 lb to the square inch – the motor is cut out by a pressure switch, and when a tap is opened the water comes out under pressure as in a town supply. When the pressure in the tank drops to say 20 lb to the square inch the motor restarts and so builds up the pressure again.

With this system there is no need to worry about levels as the pressure will push the water uphill. These tanks can be used in conjunction with either piston or centrifugal pumps.

HYDRAULIC RAMS

Hydraulic rams have the great advantage that they require no power apart from the water. When the site is suitable this is an excellent way of getting a supply. Rams do, of course, pump slowly but work continuously so the total quantity of water supplied in twenty-four hours can be considerable. It depends upon the head of water available how much can be pumped, but it takes something like a hundred gallons falling from 10′ to pump ten gallons to a height of about 75′.

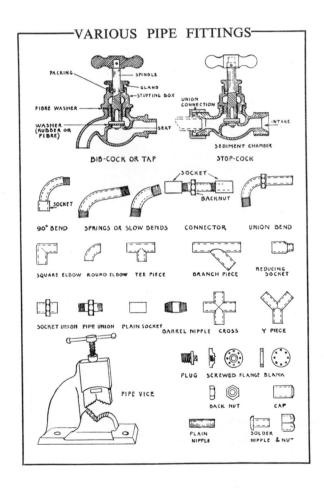

VARIOUS PIPE FITTINGS

CHAPTER XIV

FLOORS AND FITTINGS

A CONSIDERABLE amount of preliminary work is necessary before a concrete floor can be properly laid.
The area must be roughly levelled, and any hollows need making up. The levelled area then needs rolling. A garden roller will usually be sufficient, but a tractor will often do the job in far less time and with equally good results.

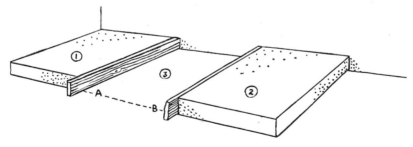

The forms should then be set up as shown in sketch. These consist of timber 1½" to 2" thick and the required depth. This depth depends upon the weight the floor will have to carry and on the soil below the concrete.

If the site is firm, 4" to 5" of concrete is ample for most practical

147

purposes, but 6″ may be required if the building is to be used for really heavy machinery.

The area is split up into suitably sized sections by the forms – 12′ is probably the maximum width but the length is not important.

FLOOR SLOPE IS IMPORTANT

Levels need to be checked. For nearly all farm buildings a slight slope of about 1″ in 12′ is an advantage, as it keeps the floor dry if the building should flood and helps to drain the floor if washed down.

With the forms in position the concrete – mixture 4 : 2 : 1 – can then be placed in position by barrow or mounted mixer. It is tipped into position and roughly spread with a shovel so that it is a little above the forms and extends from edge to edge of the form. It is then tamped down, special care being taken to see that it is well worked down against the forms.

If the area is fairly small, a board – say 7″ × 1¼″ – can be worked across to get the level and to tamp down the surface. If the area is of greater width, then a tamper as shown here is worth making.

The bays are filled alternately so that when the concrete is set in the first to be filled, the form can be removed and the remainder filled in, the set concrete now being used to carry the tamper.

CURING THE CONCRETE

Concrete should be kept damp for at least seven days so that it cures correctly, and in cold weather it must be protected from frost. (Incidentally, if concreting is being done in the winter all work must stop when the air temperature drops to freezing).

In very dry weather it will help the cure if sand is placed on the concrete as soon as it is just hard and this sand is kept wet for several days.

Concrete floors where stock will lie are best insulated. Various methods of doing this can be used.

Hollow bricks are probably the most expensive way, but you can use jam jars, bottles, cardboard tubes or corrugated asbestos

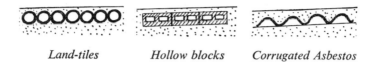

| Land-tiles | Hollow blocks | Corrugated Asbestos |

sheets. In each case the insulating materials will be placed on hardcore and then covered with a thin layer (about $1\frac{1}{2}''$) of concrete. Airspaces should always be sealed.

SIMPLE WAY OF INSULATING

One simple way of insulating a floor is to make the soil loose – either by hand, or machinery if the area is large enough – and then put paper over the whole area. Cement bags opened out will do. Make 'carrot' holes by driving an iron bar through the paper into the soil; then cover the whole area of paper with concrete to a depth of 2″, working it well down into the holes.

When the concrete sets, the earth under the paper will dry out and shrink leaving the concrete supported on the concrete 'carrots'.

These need to be about 6″ apart in each direction, and care should be taken not to tread the loose earth too much while making the holes and filling with concrete.

USE OF ELECTRIC HEATING

Floors can be both insulated and electrically heated. The current is supplied through a transformer and goes into the wire at 6 volts, This is similar to the soil-heating wires used in greenhouses for propagation work.

Do not attempt to use ordinary resistance wire for this but

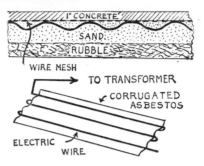

This method of electric floor heating is successfully used on a Buckinghamshire farm.

consult the suppliers of the wire made for the job and install according to their instructions.

With these general points of construction in mind, the various types of floors for different buildings can be considered.

FLOORS FOR COWSHEDS

For cowsheds the whole floor should be higher than the surrounding land and it must be laid to follow the inclination of the fall of the dung channel – about 1 in 70. It is a great mistake to keep the standings level and allow the channel to get deeper as it goes along the building.

The fall on the standing from manger to dung channel should be at least 1"; 1½" is better. The standing should be insulated.

It may be worth while enquiring about special composition for cow standings, as there are several on the market, but I have yet to hear of one which is really satisfactory over a long period.

A figure of 5' is usually given for the length of the standings, but it is an advantage in most herds to have some variation for different sizes of cows. Small breeds only require 4' 6" and the largest probably 5' 3". In any case allow for adjustment in the ties.

IMPORTANCE OF QUICK-RELEASE TIES

The central tie (york or double chain) which restricts the movement of the cow backwards and forwards has gone out of favour in recent years, and the most common type today is the side tie, usually secured by a ring sliding on a bar and capable of adjustment to suit the length of the cow.

It is essential to have a quick-release device in any chain type of tie.

Non-skid floors can be made by laying the top 1″ of the floor in granolithic concrete, consisting of two and a half parts granite chippings (¼″ down to dust) and one part cement. Finish off with wooden float.

FLOORS FOR MILKING PARLOURS

Milking parlour floors do not require insulation, but the way they slope is a matter which requires careful consideration.

It is usually said that the way the parlour floor slopes does not matter as long as there is a fall of 2″ to 5″. But it is an advantage if it falls from behind the cows towards the cows' exit. This makes for a drier floor where the workers are and also tends to keep dirty water away from the dairy.

It is usual to hose down parlours, but if the water pressure is low it is much quicker and more effective to have a trough of water behind the cows and then dip a bucket into the trough. The force behind a bucket of water carefully thrown is considerable – it will move a cow pat with ease!

VALUE OF TWO-LEVEL PARLOUR

The two-level parlour has everything to recommend it as far as saving labour is concerned, but you must bear in mind that it is a far more difficult job to convert if you wish to put it to some other use in time to come.

The same objection could be raised in connection with the tandem type of layout but this does, I think, achieve the greatest saving in labour although it may take slightly more 'machine-hours' as compared with abreast, because the machine only serves one cow and so is idle while changing over cows.

Five
Parlour
Layouts

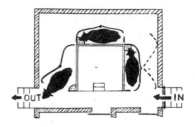

*Two-level, three units,
three stalls, one man.*

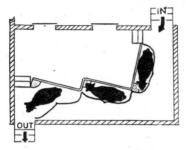

*Two-level, two or three
units, three stalls, one
man.*

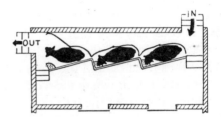

*Two-level, three units,
three stalls, one man.*

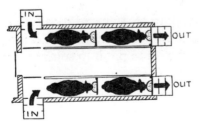

*Two-level, two units, four
stalls, one man.*

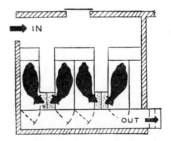

*Two-level, four units, four
stalls, one man (may need
two).*

152

This photograph illustrates type of concrete pig floor used extensively in Denmark.

First there is a 3″ layer of weak concrete (one bag cement, 3¾ cubic feet fine aggregate, 7½ cubic feet large aggregate); next a 3″ layer of no-fines concrete (one bag cement, 10 cubic feet large aggregate) then a 1″ surface finish.

The no-fines section forms the insulation and is said to stop any damp from rising.

Making a Concrete Manger

LEFT: *The shape forms, made from strong timber and lined with a smooth-surfaced material, are first placed in position and supported to prevent movement.*

BELOW: *Tamping the concrete after filling to achieve proper consolidation.*

ABOVE: *Forming the kerb. The piece of timber on the inside of the kerb should be temporarily nailed in position until the concrete is set.*

RIGHT: *A final smoothing applied by steel float. This job should be done within an hour after shaping and consolidating the concrete.*

Top picture shows a well-constructed cowhouse in which special attention has been paid to the floor to avoid its being too slippery.

The method used is to make a grout of cement, sand and a proprietary product called Cemprover. This is poured onto the floor and spread with a hair broom.

One gallon of Cemprover produces enough grout to cover 20 square yards of floor.

It is the cleanest way of working, as the milker does not walk where the cows stand.

In either type of two-level parlour the ideal arrangement is where the natural levels of surrounding land enable the cows to come in on one level and the milker and dairy to be on the lower level. Failing that, there must be steps for the cows to mount. Such steps should be not more than 10″ high and have a tread of 1′ 6″.

A better way is to have a ramp with a slope of about 2 in 7.

The difference between height of cows and milker should be between 2′ and 2′ 6″. There should be a curb to the edge of the cow standing.

FLOORS FOR PIG HOUSES

Floors for pig houses need to be so constructed that the dunging passage will stand up to the hard traffic of constant cleaning, either by hand or mechanically. It should not be insulated.

The width will depend upon how cleaning out is to be done, but it should never be less than 3′ and drainage should be arranged for each pen.

The pens themselves should be higher and should slope down to the dunging passage. The pen floors require insulation.

Feeding passage should be not less than 3′ wide with a general slope towards the door or doors, as this will make it drain freely if washed down. Not that I consider it advisable to wash down pig houses constantly; it makes the whole building far too damp and cold.

CONSTRUCTION OF WOODEN FLOORS

Wooden floors are seldom used in farm buildings except for upper floors and the construction then depends upon the anticipated load that the floor will have to carry.

In house-building it is usually considered that the safe depth of the joists can be determined by halving the span, measured in feet, call this inches and add 2″.

Taking a 16′ joist as an example: half sixteen is eight, and 8″ plus 2″ gives 10″ as the depth of the joists. These are usually set at 14″ centres.

Tongued and grooved floor boards are the most satisfactory, as if squared edge boards are used and there is any shrinkage or warping there will be spaces between boards. The heads of nails should be driven below the surface with a nail punch.

MANGERS AND TROUGHS

Mangers and troughs are the two main internal fittings which form integral parts of farm buildings.

With the increased use of more bulky food for cows there has been a tendency for the size of cowshed mangers to increase, not so much in overall size as in internal measurements. This sketch gives an idea of the old and new.

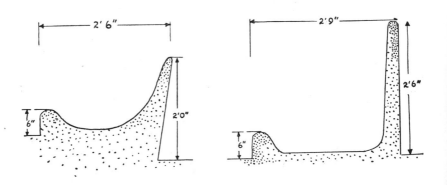

It will be noted that the fronts in both cases are 6″ high; this height should not be exceeded; if it is, there is a considerable risk of cows damaging their knees.

For mangers built in yards, allowance must be made for the probably increasing height of the manure.

For pigs, 12″ half-round salt-glazed drain channels are recommended. 'Seconds' are quite suitable and save expense. Alternatively smooth concrete of the same section can be used but this

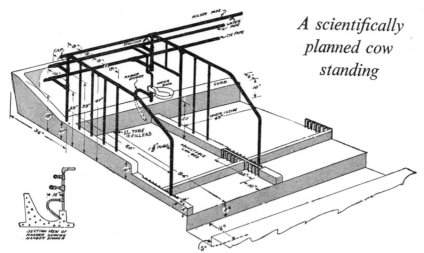

A scientifically planned cow standing

This cow-standing was designed by West Virginia University, U.S.A., after scientific study of cow behaviour. Main feature is adjustable standing length.

needs to be of the precast type of concrete, made in agitated moulds to give a very dense surface. I do not think a really satisfactory job can be done in-situ.

155

CHAPTER XV

GLAZING AND PAINTING

SHEET glass is made in various thicknesses but is described in terms of ounces per square foot, as shown below:

Ounces per sq. ft.	*Thickness of glass*
18	$\frac{1}{12}''$
24	$\frac{1}{10}''$
26	$\frac{1}{8}''$
32	$\frac{5}{32}''$

There are three grades in each weight – ordinary glazing, selected glazing and special glazing. For normal farm-building work the eighteen-ounce ordinary glazing is satisfactory, but there are times when twenty-four-ounce might be recommended for additional safety.

In particularly vulnerable positions the wired glass – with wire netting inserted in the sheets during manufacture – should be used.

Glazing is a comparatively simple job. With a putty knife put a bed of putty all round the rebate and insert the glass – this having been cut so that it is about $\frac{1}{32}$" smaller all round than the frame.

Press the glass well down onto the bed and knock in headless steel brads – called 'sprigs' – to hold the glass in position while a bevelled putty fillet is formed to cover the joint and to give additional support to the glass. In the case of steel frames there are holes into which the sprigs can be inserted.

Do not make the fillet wider than the wood or steel on the opposite side of the glass.

When the outside work is completed, trim up all surplus putty on the other side of the glass.

It is best to buy putty in a tin so that the air can be kept from any that is left over. Should it get a little hard, add a very small quantity of boiled linseed oil and work up with the hands.

GLASS-CUTTING CAN BE SIMPLE

Many people think that glass cutting is difficult, but that is not so – even with the cheap glass cutters.

The chief things to remember are how to set about the job and not to try to do it as you may have seen a professional glass-cutter do it.

He does not mark out the size to be cut, but it helps quite a lot if you do mark it with pencil and then, with a straight edge set back from the line sufficiently for the wheel of the cutter go just on the pencil line, make one steady continuous scratch from edge to edge. Don't lift the cutter unless it strays from the guide.

The secret is to make a continuous cut along the mark.

157

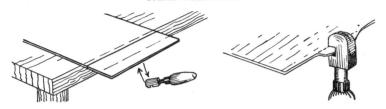

Left: tap cut section lightly from underneath. Right: snapping off a projection

When you have made the scratch line, turn the glass around until the line is parallel with the edge of the bench and projecting over a trifle. Now hold the projecting portion with one hand and, starting at one end, tap very gently all along the UNDERSIDE of the line with the metal head of the cutter.

The glass will then break away cleanly if the scratch line has been made continuously.

If little bits should still remain on the good edge they can be removed with the slots on the back of the cutter. Simply put the slot over the projection and break off.

RULES OF GOOD PAINTING

Of all repair jobs on the farm, painting is probably the one that is most often tackled by the farm staff. It can be an excellent slack-period job.

Much of this amateur painting is very well done, some is not so good – only because those doing it have not taken the trouble to master a few simple rules.

It is possible to paint wood, steel or concrete, and I will deal with each in turn. They all have one thing in common: the work must be quite dry. If you paint wet wood, then instead of preserving it you imprison in it water and exclude air – ideal conditions for the bacteria and fungi which destroy timber!

With timber, preparation of the work is most important. What form this takes depends on whether the timber is new or old.

For new timber the surface should be reasonably smooth and brushed free from dust. Then the knots should be sealed with a knot stopper. This can be a proprietary kind; or you can apply two thin coats of shellac dissolved in methylated spirits. Either will prevent the resin 'bleeding through' the finished job and so spoiling the work.

THE PRIMING COAT

For the priming coat use the specially prepared priming paint sold for this purpose. Often this can stand some expanding with turps and boiled linseed oil – up to a quarter of a pint of each to each pint of paint – but it just depends upon the wood how much it can be expanded; the more absorbent it is, the more oil you can add.

If you have not got any priming paint by you and you want to get on with the job, you can use finishing paint provided you add three quarts of boiled linseed oil and two and half quarts of turps to each gallon. This will be quite satisfactory for priming.

The thing to bear in mind regarding the priming coat is that what you have to do is supply enough oil to satisfy the wood and leave a skin of paint on the surface.

The priming coat must be thoroughly dry before the next coat is applied. This coat is just as it comes from the tin. If thinning is required use turps and boiled linseed oil in equal quantities – unless you intend to put on three coats in which case only use turps for thinning the second coat. This will make a harder surface.

The final coat can be thinned with linseed which gives it a good gloss and extra waterproofing.

PREPARING OLD TIMBER

For painting old work greater care is needed in the preparation of the surfaces.

Loose paint needs removing with a wire brush. If it has blistered and peeled use a blowlamp and scraper or an electric paint remover. Glass-paper can sometimes be used or even a putty knife.

159

There are also proprietary paint removers which will usually enable the paint to be removed two minutes after being brushed on. Unlike caustic soda these removers do not harm the timber nor do they irritate the skin of the worker, but some of them are highly inflammable.

When the old paint is smooth, any cracks or nail holes will need to be filled with putty. On new work it is usual to putty these after the priming coat has been applied. If putty is applied to new timber before the priming coat, the oil will be drawn out into the timber.

If the surface of old timber is very porous, it will need a priming coat just the same as new work. Otherwise two or three coats of finishing paint should be given as explained for new timber.

ESTIMATING AMOUNT OF PAINT

The amount of paint required for timber can be very roughly got from the following:

1 gallon undercoating covers 400 square feet.
1 gallon second coat covers 350 square feet.

But this must be regarded as a rough guide only; varying surfaces may easily absorb much more or less than these quantities.

Probably more bad work is caused by bad mixing than by anything else. So do see that paint is thoroughly mixed before starting work. It helps quite a lot to stand tins upside down overnight. And if you use raw linseed oil at any time, add half a pint of Japan drier to each gallon of oil.

TAKING CARE OF PAINT

It does not matter how carefully you put the lid on a partly used tin of paint it will have a skin on the surface when you open it again a few weeks later. This skin must be strained off before the paint is used or you will have bits and pieces on the work.

A simple way of preventing the formation of skin is to set the open tin level on a shelf and then gently pour sufficient turps to

160

Examples

of

Well-Lit

Farm

Buildings

ABOVE: *A food store in which efficiency can be the watchword – largely influenced by exceptionally good lighting.*

LEFT: *Even a passage between buildings has a business-like air about it if it is adequately lit.*

The three composite pictures show how exterior lighting can be put to good use. Inset picture shows method of attachment to the building; top picture shows the brilliant light itself; bottom picture is of the other end of the yard – well lit for working purposes.

cover the surface with a layer $\frac{1}{8}''$ thick. Then put the lid on and all you will have to do when you want it is to mix up the paint.

TAKING CARE OF BRUSHES

Hundreds of brushes must be used for one job only and then wasted because someone leaves them in the paint or puts them in water to keep them soft, but forgets all about them and when the water evaporates they set hard.

Even if you are going to use them the next day it is worth while taking the time to wash them thoroughly in paraffin and dry them on a cloth. They can then be stored dry.

If you keep them in a mixture of linseed and water, do not simply stand them in the tin or they will become bent. Suspend them as shown here:

A little trouble saves a lot of trouble.

PREPARING NEW GALVANIZED SHEETS

New galvanized steel sheets should not be painted until they have weathered for some weeks. If you are in a hurry to get on with the painting you can speed up the work by treating the sheets with a mixture of 4 oz hydrochloric acid, 4 oz copper sulphate and 1 gallon of water. This is applied with a brush and then rubbed with steel wool. The same effect can be achieved by painting on vinegar or ammonia and rubbing with steel wool.

Black steel is always covered with a bluish-grey film of scale as a result of the rolling process. Commercially this film is removed with acid, but if you leave it for a short time in the open it will rust and this can be taken off with a wire brush.

REMOVING RUST

With old steel the rust must be removed. This can be done with rust remover or you can rub the surface with paraffin and then with steel wool dipped in linseed oil. If it is very rusty, dip the linseed-oiled steel wool into pumice powder and rub hard.

When the rust has been removed, rub over with a cloth dipped in linseed oil and finish off with a dry cloth to remove most of the oil.

When rust has been removed with a wire brush the steel should always be rubbed down with a linseed-oiled cloth to remove all dust.

If new concrete is painted it will not be satisfactory, as the alkaline substances will affect the paint, but again you need not wait for it to weather down as you can paint on a mixture of zinc sulphate and water mixed at the rate of 3 lb to the gallon. As soon as this is dry, paint can be applied.

USE OF BITUMEN PAINT

So far we have discussed oil paint, but for all farm work – and more especially buildings such as dutch barns – bitumen paint has much to recommend it. It can be obtained in many colours and has covering ability at least equal to oil paint and under some circumstances far more. On smooth, non-absorbent surfaces one gallon may cover 1,000 square feet.

Only use the special thinners supplied by the makers of bitumen paint, and do not apply bitumen on top of lead paint.

Bitumen paint is very good for concrete.

162

Synthetic paints of various types have been produced and are well worth considering where there is a lot of washing down to be done.

USING A SPRAY GUN

More and more painting is being done with spraying machines. Good work can be done with them in a very short time – provided the operator takes the trouble to get the technique right. The gun must always be at right angles to the work and about eight inches

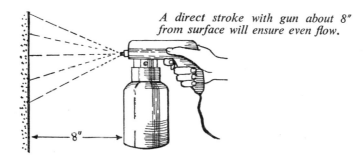

A direct stroke with gun about 8" from surface will ensure even flow.

away from it. The strokes must be of even speed and the trigger must be released at the end of each stroke.

Paint has to be thinner for use in spray guns. Special thinners are available – these evaporate rapidly and leave the paint in the same state as if it had been applied with a brush.

MACHINE MUST BE CLEANED

It is essential that the gun and all parts of the machine through which paint passes are cleaned at the end of the day's work. Once paint has been allowed to set in them you might as well write them off, as it is almost impossible to get them clean again.

This is perhaps one of the disadvantages of spraying. You need to have a fair amount of straightforward work to do at one time or the time spent in cleaning the plant is not justified.

MIXING WHITEWASH

While whitewash can be purchased in tins ready for mixing with water, it is quite expensive if you have a fair amount of work to do.

Burnt lime used to be the basis of whitewash, but hydrated lime – which is a standard product obtainable everywhere – is the better ingredient. It must, however, be fresh stock.

It is best to make the lime into lime putty first. This seems to make it work more smoothly. To make lime putty you need a shallow container – a wash tub is excellent. Put in 1 gallon of water for each 7lb of lime that is to be mixed. Sprinkle the lime in evenly and keep stirring with a broad board. Then leave undisturbed for eighteen hours. It will remain fit for use for a week at least.

When you are going to use it, mix 2 lb of common salt in two-thirds of a gallon of water and as much lime putty that has been made from 7 lb of lime.

It is best to add the salt water slowly so that it makes a cream first and then goes down to the correct whitewash consistency.

CEMENT WASHES

That mixture is suitable for all ordinary work on the farm, but if you want a high-quality cement whitewash, dissolve 2 lb salt in 1 gallon of hot water, allow to cool and then mix with lime putty made from 7 lb of lime. When well mixed add 1 lb of cement.

As a rough guide to the quantity required, a gallon of whitewash will cover 200 square feet in a first coat on wood and probably increase to 250 square feet on plaster or brick. The second coat will probably cover 25 per cent more. It is nearly always advisable to have two coats.

On straightforward work a man can usually put on about a gallon per hour with a brush and probably three gallons with a spray.

It is essential that the work should be thoroughly cleaned down before starting to apply whitewash. It will not adhere if there is any loose material, grease or dried manure.

A WARNING

Cement paints, although more trouble, have a greater life than lime washes. They can be washed down without harm to the surface. It should be remembered that they cannot be applied on top of old whitewash or oil paints; these must be removed first if you wish to use cement paint.

Three coats are usually required and they need moisture during the hardening period. Try not to apply in direct sunlight, and in hot weather spray the surface with water a short time before applying the paint and again after about six hours of drying.

Cement paints can be applied with a brush or spray but the quantity mixed must be used up within three or four hours of mixing, as settling will be taking place by that time. When a spray is used it is essential to strain the mixture very carefully and to wash the plant out immediately work stops.

PRESERVING TIMBER

While oak and larch will stand a considerable amount of weathering without decay, nearly all other timbers in common use must be treated to preserve them.

There are some proprietary preparations available, but the most common one is creosote and it will give very good protection provided the timber is dry when it is applied. It is almost useless to apply it to damp timber.

The proper treatment is to put the timber in a tank of creosote and then heat it up to about 180° F for two hours and allow to stand for twenty-four hours. The heat drives air and water from the timber and this is replaced by creosote being drawn into it.

Timber rots quickest where there is a changing temperature and damp conditions. A gate-post, for instance, rots at ground level first – the parts below the ground and above are usually quite sound when the post breaks off at ground level.

CREOSOTING POSTS

The simple way of creosoting posts on the farm is to have a drum – say an old 40-gallon oil drum – set up in the open with an open top and stand the posts in this and then pour creosote in to the required depth. Light a fire underneath and bring the temperature up. Bear in mind that if you have any leaks you may have a fire, as creosote will ignite quite readily.

The upper parts of the post can be brushed, but they will require repeated dressings if their life is to be greatly extended.

If you are creosoting rough fencing posts take the bark off before putting them into the tank or you will waste a lot of creosote by absorption into it.

CHAPTER XVI

INSTALLING ELECTRICITY

MANY farmers in this country do not make full use of electricity when it is available; some do not have it connected to the farm because of the high connection charges made by the supply authorities.

Both of these positions are brought about by farmers not appreciating the possible scope of electricity to increase production to save labour and so to increase profits in the end.

A farmer cannot do much about the high cost of connection or installation. Indeed, unless he has considerable experience he should not attempt the wiring. There is nothing more dangerous, both from a fire risk point of view or even death to people and stock, than badly installed electric wiring.

MAKE FULL USE OF IT

When electricity is brought to the farm it should be used as a tractor is used – as fully as possible.

Plan on the assumption that there will be increased use made of it as time goes on, and if a fair amount of work can be found for motors of more than 3 h.p. then have a three-phase supply.

This is at about 400 volts, whereas the single-phase is about 230 volts. It will be installed so that the large motors work off the three-phase circuits and the small motors and lights etc. will be on the single-phase circuits.

The advantage of doing this is that three-phase motors are cheaper to buy and cost slightly less to run.

GROUP MACHINES TOGETHER

It saves considerably in the cost of wiring if machines which are likely to require large motors are grouped together as far as possible – a point worth bearing in mind when designing a new layout.

It as a great advantage to have 15-amp, 3-pin sockets fitted in all buildings – although there may be no immediate need for them. They are invaluable for plugging-in various hand tools, inspection lamps, and even motors up to 4 h.p. which may be required from time to time on repair work.

PLAN LIGHTING CAREFULLY

The time spent on carefully planning the layout of the lighting of farm buildings will soon be repaid by the extra efficiency obtained.

I consider there should be sufficient light to carry on with work at any time of the year in any building. Apart from the initial cost of installing extra lighting points they cost nothing unless they are being used.

Whether one installs filament or fluorescent lighting depends very largely on the ability to spend capital for the latter or being prepared to spend more on running costs of the former over the years.

These sketches show typical layouts with filament and fluorescent lighting. The eight filament lamps may cost £12 to install, and

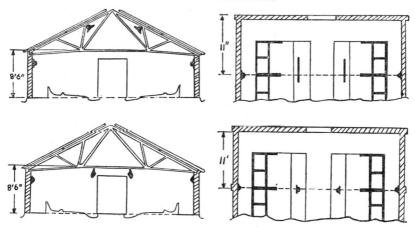

Top sketches show sensible lighting layout with fluorescent lighting. Below, with filament lighting. But there's a difference in costs.

cost £6 5*s* to run for 1,000 hours; whereas six fluorescent would probably cost £60 to install but would cost only £3 10*s* to run for 1,000 hours – taking electricity at 1*d* per unit in both cases.

The practical answer is probably to have fluorescent lights where they are required for a considerable number of hours in the year – such as the cowshed – and filament lamps elsewhere.

The position of the lights is most important. So is the position of control switches; they should be instantly accessible without fumbling and so placed that lights can be turned on and off as one passes through buildings – so avoiding the need to retrace your steps to turn a light off.

The use of ceiling switches – operated by a cord – have much to commend them in many farm buildings and can save a certain amount of cost in the installation in many cases.

The lighting of open yards is important and is best achieved as shown in the photograph facing page 161.

In pig houses make provision for plugging in heaters for the young pigs.

If electric fences are used on the farm and the layout lends itself to the use of a mains electric fencer, this can be fixed in position where it will not be damaged. Control switches can be made at

Showing (left) good light placing. Right, the cow's udder is in darkness.

various points where the fencing wire is carried out of the buildings.

The farm workshop probably requires more light than any part of the farm, and provision should be made in it for the use – now or in the future – of electric welding plant. If the wiring is suitable for the load of an electric welder it will be ample for any other electric tools which are likely to be used on any farm.

A SATISFACTORY CABLE

Vulcanized rubber-insulated cable is very satisfactory for farm wiring. Indeed it is the only practical system which can be adopted if the cost is to be kept within reason.

The alleged risk of rats attacking this cable is negligible if the wires are run clear of rat runs. In any case with modern rat poison being so effective there is little excuse for a farm having any number of rats about.

Wires should be run as high as possible in the buildings to prevent accidental damage. When they do have to come down to a level which is within reach of stock they should be carefully guarded with metal; conduit piping is best. When lamps are installed in a position where there is a risk of damage they should be installed in bulk-head fittings.

HINT ABOUT MOTORS

When motors have to be installed some distance from a wall then the wires crossing from the wall to the motor must be adequately protected. Conduit is suitable; it may need a 'bridge' of wood if, say, sack trolleys are likely traffic over it.

If a permanent diagram showing the position of all cable runs can be provided at the main switch control it may be of considerable help in the servicing of the system in years to come.

FACTS YOU SHOULD KNOW

The efficiency and safety of any electrical installation depends upon the skill and knowledge of those who install it. While it is not a job to be lightly undertaken by anyone, it may be of some assistance to know a little more about installations in farm buildings.

As vulcanized rubber cables are excellent for the job it is simple to run them without a lot of cutting away and making up. They can be fixed with cleats or ferry metal clips.

All joints must be made in junction boxes. If there is any risk of damp getting into them, fill them up with waterproofing compound such as 'Kalanoid'. Where switches or fittings have to be exposed to the weather get watertight ones and run the cable to them through conduit.

CABLE SIZES

Always see the size of the cable used is ample for the current that it will have to carry – not only now but in the future. This also applies to switches, etc. The suppliers of the cables and fittings will always advise you if you tell them the length of cable involved and the maximum load which will be put on.

Use separate fuses for each circuit, and avoid having too many lights on one circuit or a blown fuse will put a large number of lights out.

While it is usual to wire lights in parallel, where lights have to be dimmed – such as in poultry pens – then the use of a series circuit may be useful. While one lamp is on you get full light and when the 'two-way-and-off' switch is put in the other position it puts the lamps in series and so gives a dim light.

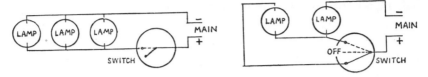

Left: a normal lighting circuit. Right: circuit to give dimming.

The use of two-way switches for light control is invaluable. The circuit A shown here covers this, but if you have already got an existing switch and wish to make it two-way control without altering the existing wiring, then follow sketch B.

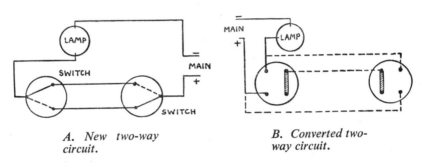

A. New two-way circuit.

B. Converted two-way circuit.

PUT SWITCHES IN RIGHT LEAD

It is essential that switches are always put in the correct lead. I will call it the positive lead although many will object to the term as A.C. current does not have a positive and negative. However, it is the lead which shows a flash on a neon tester, and provided the switch is put in that lead it ensures that the point is quite dead when the switch is open.

If the switch is put in the negative lead, current will always be passing through the point – making this 'live' – although the switch may be open.

It will be appreciated that under those circumstances anyone could get a shock off a point when changing a bulb or doing anything else in the neighbourhood of the fitting despite having taken the precaution of seeing that the switch was off.

The testers referred to are often in the form of a screwdriver and cost only a few shillings. They are very useful for checking faults, as you have simply to put the point of one against a wire or element you are testing and you can see if the current is there by the flash of the small neon bulb in the handle of the tester.

When making alterations to wiring always switch off at the main box and take the fuses out and put them in your pocket. Then you know you are safe!

CHAPTER XVII

TEMPORARY BUILDINGS

T HERE are many occasions when a temporary building is useful, either for housing implements or stock.

But, even though it is temporary, it wants to be built so that it will last long enough to justify the cost of erection.

The most commonly used material for this purpose is straw. One snag is that a straw building is untidy and is often kept in use long after its usefulness is over – which really shows that a permanent building was probably necessary in the first place. Another snag is the risk of fire – you should certainly consult your insurance company before housing stock or implements in such a building.

CHOOSE SITE CAREFULLY

In any case a straw building should be erected on a site which is well away from other buildings so that when its useful life is finished you can salvage any useful materials – such as poles and wire netting – and then burn the remainder without endangering any other buildings.

The site for any straw building should also be reasonably dry, and water from the roof should be drawn away in channels or the bottom of the walls will soon rot.

There are two main ways of building, one with bales and the other with packed straw between wire netting.

It is necessary to stiffen walls of bales with poles if they are to go up to any height and also to 'bond' the layers – as in brick-laying. Bottom bales should be set on edge so that the wires do not come in contact with the soil.

PROTECT AGAINST STOCK

To stop stock pulling the straw out it is necessary to fence with wire netting for pigs or poultry or with rails for cattle. I have been told that if you creosote baled straw cattle will not touch it, but I have had no experience of this.

In the case of cattle you can put a fence 5′ inside the walls and use this to put fresh straw in each day for the cattle to eat by

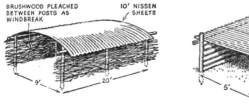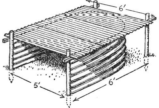

Two examples of simple temporary farm buildings.
Left: shelter for grazing sows. Right: an in-the-field farrowing hut.

putting their heads over the fence. What they do not eat is thrown into the yard each day before the new lot is put in.

The amount of straw required to build in bales is considerable, even if the walls are only 2′ wide. A yard 45′ long and 30′ wide with walls 8′ high on three sides (the south side being a rail fence) will require 250 bales for the walls alone.

METHOD OF BUILDING BALES

To attempt to save straw by building a wall with all bales on edge would be inadvisable, even with a lot of poles set fairly close

How to Build with Bales

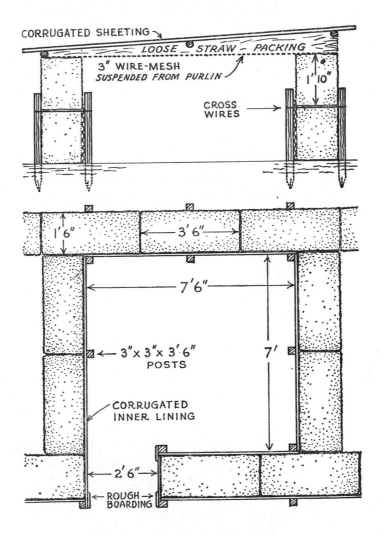

CORRUGATED SHEETING

LOOSE STRAW PACKING

3" WIRE-MESH
SUSPENDED FROM PURLIN

1' 10"

CROSS WIRES

1' 6"

3' 6"

7' 6"

7'

3" x 3" x 3' 6" POSTS

CORRUGATED INNER LINING

2' 6"

ROUGH BOARDING

This modest straw-bale house, which would be suitable for pigs or calves, illustrates the basic principles of straw-bale building – the lower layers held rigidly in position, protected from stock, and a roof pitch obtained by loose straw packing.

176

ABOVE: *A strongly constructed temporary stockyard made from farm poles, wire and straw.*

BELOW: *Another way – particularly useful for pigs and young stock – of weather protection with posts, wire and straw. Here loose straw is sandwiched between two layers of pig netting.*

A temporary building particularly suitable for pigs. Rough farm posts with corrugated sheeting provide the main structure; straw-packed hurdles, secured by iron bars through metal eyes, form the walls and 'gate'.

Two particularly good examples of temporary buildings with straw bales. Note the method of bonding in building the walls.

In structures of the type in the lower picture, where stock have greater freedom, both the inside and the outside of the walls are better protected with netting to ensure a longer life.

With temporary buildings, protection of the straw can be
achieved by reinforcing wire strips as shown in the top
picture.
The same material can be used to make small stockyards.

together. So if you are short of straw, the better way is to build with straw-packed wire-netting walls.

Set pairs of poles about 9″ apart with 5′ between each pair. Wire-netting is then put along each row of poles and wire ties across the width of the wall. The space between the wire is then packed with straw, well pressed down to form a 9″ wall.

Use 4″-mesh netting for cattle; 2″-mesh for calves and pigs.

PROBLEMS OF ROOFING

Roofs are sometimes a problem, more especially when the span is considerable. For short lengths of roof; poles can support it and loose straw placed on and thatched in, or you can stretch sheep netting along from poles and thatch this.

Another way is to have poles along and fix corrugated steel sheets with nuts and bolts so that it can be recovered in due course. A layer of straw underneath will prevent condensation.

CHAPTER XVIII

ROADS AND FENCES

W ITH modern transport, good roads have become almost essential for all farms.

By good I do not mean an arterial type of road wide enough to take all types of traffic in both directions at speed! – that would be just a waste of money and land – but a reasonably level, hard surface, wide enough to take any normal vehicle is what is required.

It is worth remembering that a 9′ wide road will have all the wheels running in the same two grooves, whereas a 12′-wide road allows them to be spread over.

CONSIDER LOCAL MATERIALS

Many think first of concrete roads and when they have considered the cost turn to other possibilities. I think the other way. Concrete is essential around the buildings and in yards, but away from there there is a great deal to be said for making a road of local materials.

It will nearly always be far cheaper than concrete, easier to build, easier to repair if it should get damaged and requires only slightly more maintenance.

By local materials I mean stone, chalk, gravel or cinders, all of which can be used to make excellent roads.

But there are two points to remember in building a road. The first is that the weight of the traffic is – ultimately – carried on the subsoil. The second is that few subsoils will carry a load unless they are dry.

KEEP SUBSOIL DRY

Therefore roads should be designed to keep the subsoil dry. It is almost useless to build in very wet conditions unless the water can be got away.

While the usual method is to dig out the soil to make the site of a road there is really much to commend the idea of putting the road material on the soil surface and so making it a little higher than the surrounding land.

If it is a new road, turf will have to be removed and this can be stacked to form edges to the road. Then, when the road has been completed, it and its verges will be a little above the other land. So it will keep dry.

The most serious condition for any road is to have water standing on, or running down its surface. You see many quite good farm roads ruined by their being sited in a hollow or on a slope. The water runs down and takes off the surface and then makes deep channels.

DEALING WITH SURFACE WATER

In planning a new road this sort of thing has to be avoided but if you have already got one in that state you must set about putting 'grips' or cuttings into the verges of the road to carry this water off. It may even involve digging a drain and inserting a grating in the road; this is very seldom necessary but it may be the only way of preventing water running down the road.

Practically all roads, except concrete, are flexible. If you look carefully at the surface as a very heavy lorry passes along you will see it bends in front of the wheels!

This will not do any harm when the occasional heavy lorry comes over a road built for medium-weight traffic. There is no need to build for the heaviest possible load that the road may have to carry.

In the case of concrete it is rather different, as if a load did break the surface the road would be ruined and repairing it would be a difficult job. One advantage of the flexible road is that it is fairly easy to repair in the event of damage, although it requires rather more maintenance over a period of years.

CHIEF POINTS TO WATCH

If you build a flexible road the chief points to watch are:

1. That the site is reasonably dry when the work is done.
2. That the material used is well compacted as it is put down.
3. That the surface is made watertight, if possible with tar or bitumen.
4. That water is carried away from the road and not allowed to stand or run along the surface.
5. That mud is cleared off. Tyres will pick up the surface if this is not done. (Mud can even spoil a concrete road in this way.)

MAKING CONCRETE ROADS

Concreting for roads is much the same as for floors – see Chapter X – but it is necessary to place stuntheads every 20′ or so.

The timber is removed before starting the next length – if the concrete has had time to set; but if not you can concrete up to each side of the stunthead and then very carefully remove it so as not to damage the tamped edge and fill in the space with concrete.

Do not use the road, except for light traffic, for a fortnight.

The other system of concreting a farm road is the Cheecol method which is of considerable interest to farmers, as it saves quite a lot of work in concrete mixing.

The job is done by first putting broken stone or some other hardcore rubble – no piece should be greater than half the depth of the finished job – down between the side forms.

The cement, sand and water are then mixed together with the Cheecol chemical and poured over the hardcore until it rises to the level of the forms. It is then tamped off and the job is done.

GROUTED WHEEL TRACKS

The same method may be used for grouted wheel tracks.

These tracks are quite cheap to lay, using – in many cases – implements already on the farm, for much of the work, and there is little real excuse for many of the muddy tracks we see on farms today.

You do not need to level the ground but to follow the natural contour.

If the soil is suitable, simply plough out two tracks each 2' wide and 4" deep and fill these with broken stone. Then pour a 6 : 1 ballast-and-cement mixture over them until they are level with or just above, the surrounding soil.

When the concrete commences to set, the edges can be trimmed up with a spade.

Single tracks can be made in a similar way to enable cows to come to and from cowsheds without walking through a lot of mud.

CATTLE GRIDS

Cattle grids are becoming more and more common, as they save not only the waste of time opening and closing gates but also prevent other people leaving gates open.

On my farm I use grids as shown in the photograph between pages 184-5. These are reasonable in cost and easy to put down. All one has to do is to dig a shallow hole about 15" deep and put a layer of concrete over the whole of the site. When this is set, the precast sections are put down on mortar and the job is complete.

It will be appreciated that this type of grid has the advantage that if an animal should be pushed by another onto the grid it cannot put its legs down between two bars – as is possible with a bar grid.

FARM-BUILT GRIDS

Farmers who prefer to build their own grids will find the following of assistance.

The site needs a hole about 3' deep, 9' wide and 8' long. Concrete should be laid over the whole of the bottom of the hole and

The cattle grid on the left is inadequately fenced. Stock will attempt to 'edge' round the posts.

A better form of fencing is shown on right. Stock cannot get past it. A wide stock gate or a narrow gate for people can be let into the fence near to the grid if required.

then dwarf walls erected to carry the tubes. The size of the tubes and the probable weight that the grid will have to carry will determine the number of walls required.

The tubes should be not more than 4" apart.

There are many methods which can be used for locating them, the simple way being to have them dropping into groves on the walls. But do have some means of locking them in position or you may get children taking the bars out – with serious results. It is an advantage to be able to remove the bars for cleaning out the pit from time to time.

The site of any grid should be such that it is in the direct line of traffic. The by-pass gate for stock and people should be off-set to one side.

BUILDING A CULVERT

Few roads can be built without some culverts and so we can deal with these here.

Try to make all culverts large enough to take the greatest probable amount of water which will come at any time of the year, and allow for the fact that most culverts will, from time to time, be partly blocked with stones or rubbish.

Stones can often be prevented from going into the culvert if a catchpit is built at the top end. The size of this catchpit will be

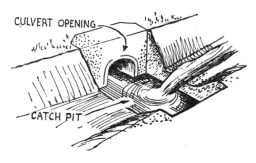

Diagrammatic sketch of culvert construction.

governed by the conditions that are likely to prevail under storm conditions.

THE EASIEST WAY

The easiest way of building a culvert is to have large collared pipes and set these on a firm foundation in a dry time, making the joints with a 1 : 1 mixture of cement and sand.

Then at each end put up shuttering or brickwork and fill in around the pipes with concrete; a 9 : 1 mixture of gravel-as-dug and cement will be strong enough for this.

THE CHEAPEST WAY

These pipes do become rather expensive in the larger sizes and then it is much cheaper to form the arch with corrugated steel sheets and concrete over them, reinforcing if necessary. The sheets will in time rust away, but that is not important as they are only there as shuttering until the concrete has set.

When that concrete has set then the roadway can be carried over in the same material as the rest of the road.

Whatever method is used to build the culvert it is advisable to extend concrete beyond the outlet for 3′ or 4′ on the bed of the ditch, as water coming out of a culvert will often wash a really deep hole which can in time undermine the end of the job.

PRINCIPLES OF GOOD FENCING

Having gone so far as to discuss roadmaking in a book about farm buildings, I might as well go a step farther and deal briefly with fencing – an important aspect of road and yard construction.

Making a really good fence is an expensive job and the labour involved is much the same whether the materials used have a short life or a long one and it is for that reason I feel that if a wire fence is to be erected it should be made of durable materials.

Concrete posts are well worth considering. They can be made on the farm but I do not recommend it, as unless they are really well made frost will quickly damage them. Further it is very difficult to make a lot of really good posts without the aid of the special equipment which manufacturers have at their disposal.

Before placing an order for concrete posts make sure the suppliers will send posts with holes at the correct distance apart – many standard spacings are quite useless for holding stock!

Photograph on the left shows the work of setting the side forms in position.
Then, as shown below, the stunt-heads are set at right angles to the side forms at intervals of about 20'.

Concreting
a
Farm Road

The side forms should be level if the road is to be arched in the centre to drain rain water each side; or there should be a cross fall of about 1" in 40". (See also pictures on next page.)

The stuntheads require pegging firmly as shown in left-hand photograph.
BELOW: *The tamper should be used until the concrete is well consolidated and has formed a fairly smooth tightly-knit surface. The correct finish can usually be obtained in two or three runs of the tamper.*

Grouted Wheel Tracks

With cord lines to mark the width of the track, about 4″ of top soil should be excavated and a bedding of hardcore or rubble laid down. (See also further pictures overleaf.)

A cement grout (1 bag cement, 2½ cu. ft. sand, 7 gallons water is poured over the large stones and (inset picture) the surface is finished off with a stiff broom and the edges cut clean with a spade as the concrete hardens.

This type of cattle grid can be purchased complete, ready for setting on a concrete base.

Picture below shows one in position on the author's farm.

Concrete posts shown here are pierced at intervals for standard fencing wire. But in this case economy has been effected by using them as permanent posts for electric fencing by fixing an insulator to each post.

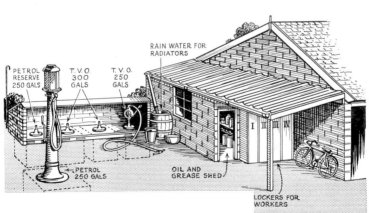

PETROL
RESERVE
250 GALS

T.V.O.
300
GALS

T.V.O.
250
GALS

RAIN WATER FOR
RADIATORS

PETROL
250 GALS

OIL AND
GREASE SHED

LOCKERS FOR
WORKERS

Photograph and diagrammatic sketch show a business-like arrangement of fuel pumps and servicing equipment at one end of a farm implements and tractor shed.

The following table may be of some assistance in spacing wires:

FOR	GAUGE NO. OF WIRE	SPACING (*from the ground*) (b) *indicates barbed wire*			TOTAL HEIGHT
Cattle only	3	20″	10″	12″(b)	3′ 6″
Cattle and sheep	6	5″ 8″(b)	6″ 9″	7″ 10″(b)	3′ 9″
Cattle, sheep and lambs	7	4″ 7″(b)	5″ 8″	6″ 9″(b)	3′ 3″
Pigs		Woven wire fencing is the only satisfactory fence			

It is assumed that all posts will be 4′ above ground and 3′ below ground. Straining posts should not be more than 150 yards apart

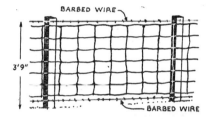 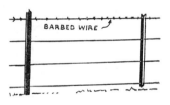

Left: The only satisfactory form of permanent fencing for pigs. Right: typical cattle fencing, using angle-iron main posts with droppers.

on a straight run but they must be placed whenever there is a change of direction.

Without droppers – strips of metal which keep the wires the correct distance apart – posts should be about 9′ apart, but for economy in both labour and materials droppers are recommended. If two are used between each two posts, the distance between posts can be increased to about 20′.

USE A POST-HOLE DIGGER

If the fencing job is of any size it is well worth while buying or hiring a post-hole digger to fit on a tractor. Not only is it speedy but it digs a straight hole with a small diameter which can be filled with concrete after the post has been set in, or, of course, well rammed with earth.

Where the fence crosses a dip a concrete block can be sunk in the ground – use as a mould a 5-gallon oil drum with both ends out, putting a loop of iron in one end as you make it. Then, when

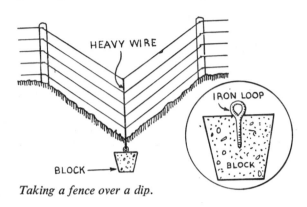

HEAVY WIRE

IRON LOOP

BLOCK

BLOCK

Taking a fence over a dip.

the fence is erected, a piece of plain fencing wire is twisted round each run of wire at the correct distance and connected to the loop in the block before the fence is tightened up.

There are several types of strainers, but the cheapest (and as good as any) is the straining eye-bolt.

For fixing wires to concrete posts use hair-pin staples, they are

A hair-pin staple.   *A straining eye-bolt*

easily fixed and if a post should get broken it can be easily replaced without taking the fence down.

Eight-gauge wire is satisfactory for almost any conditions. It gives about 550 yards to the cwt of plain wire or 675 yards of the stranded type. While plain wire is more commonly used, there is a lot to recommend the stranded – this being seven strands twisted

together. It is much easier to work with, but it does cost rather more than the plain.

Barbed wire is sold in 220-yard reels with points 3" apart. This gives 530 yards to the cwt. With points 6" apart you get 600 yards to the cwt.

FENCING ACROSS A DITCH

When a fence crosses ditches which will have a considerable amount of water at some times of the year it is worth making a baffle as shown in the sketch:

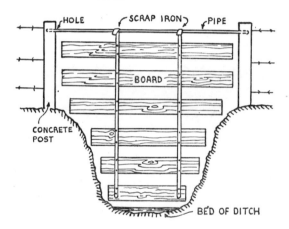

When erecting chain-link or woven-wire fencing, straining can only be effected by threading a piece of pipe or wood through the end of the roll and then pulling upon that.

While this type of fence is absolutely stockproof if the correct size is ordered, pigs will attempt to get under and it is advisable to run a strand of barbed wire along the bottom and for cattle another one along the top.

CHAPTER XIX

BUILDING A STOCK YARD

THE farmyard used to be an open space in the centre of a set of farm buildings; today it has become one of the largest parts of most buildings and more often than not it is covered.

Open yards have the disadvantage that rainfall in many parts of the country is so heavy that the straw will not absorb both rain and urine, and so drainage is necessary.

This results in a loss of manurial value. Nevertheless drainage is essential if the subsoil is non-porous, and the yard floor should be sloped to a collecting pit where a road-type grating can be set over a catchpit, say 2' × 2'. From this 6" pipes can be run to a rather larger catchpit, say 3' × 3' and from that 4" land drains can go to a ditch.

The 6" pipes need to be so placed that drain rods can be easily used to clear any stoppage. It is essential to remember to clean the catchpits from time to time.

All yards should face south if possible and be walled up to a height of at least 8' on the north and east sides.

It may not always be possible to arrange protection on those sides when yards are being added to existing buildings, but which-

ever walls are used for protection they should adjoin and not be opposite. When they adjoin they give a protected corner; if they are opposite they create a 'wind tunnel' – especially if the yard is covered.

ADVANTAGE OF COVERING

Whenever possible, yards should be at least partly covered; not only does this give greater comfort to the stock but also to the workers. And it prevents wastage by drainage.

For partly covered yards the shelter should, if possible, be on the north side; failing that the east. If on the west or south it will get a lot of bad weather blowing into it.

The height should be at least 11′ clear to allow for front-mounted loaders to work in reasonable comfort and at least 15′ in width is desirable. The roof construction should be such that the minimum of stanchions are required.

For fully-covered yards the question of the number of stanchions is a problem; if they are reduced to a minimum then the cost of the roof will be considerably increased because the span is likely to be quite wide.

But as all yards need dividing up into areas of 1,500 to 2,000 square feet, stanchions can often be arranged so that they come in line with the dividing fences. Often the stanchions can also form the hanging posts for gates, which saves the cost of separate gate-posts.

The method of erection is exactly as for framed buildings, described in Chapter VII.

AVOIDING CONDENSATION

Condensation from the roof of a covered yard can be considerable, especially when corrugated steel is used. Even with asbestos cement sheeting it can be quite a snag.

This can be greatly reduced by having a 'saw-tooth' roof as shown on the next page.

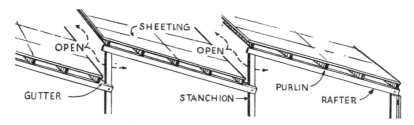

The saw-tooth type of roof.

The openings should face south; some rain will blow in at times, but the sun will also shine in and the air will always be fresh.

The self-feeding of silage is going to make many farmers consider how they can adapt their yards to this great labour-saving idea, as has been done in the arrangement shown below.

I feel it is essential with self-fed silage that there is a concrete floor and that provision is made for draining, both from the silage pit area and from the yard.

It must be so arranged that filling can be done off a ramp unless

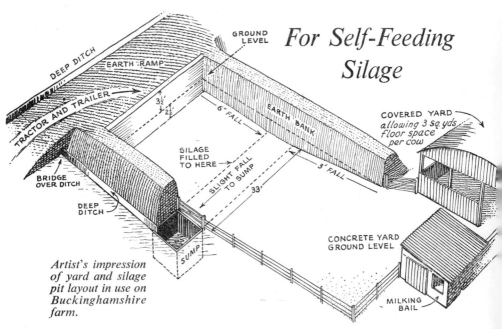

For Self-Feeding Silage

Artist's impression of yard and silage pit layout in use on Buckinghamshire farm.

190

baled silage is to be stored, although even in that case provision should be made for driving a tractor up and off the silage as it will need to be consolidated.

I am sure it would be even better to have a roof to cover the whole of the silage area, as this would keep out rain and make for greater comfort for the stock in the winter.

USE OF ROOF 'APRONS'

The use of 'aprons' on the roofs of yards can be of considerable help in reducing the number of obstructions around the yard. These offer, too, an easy way of joining onto an existing building – if this is done as follows:

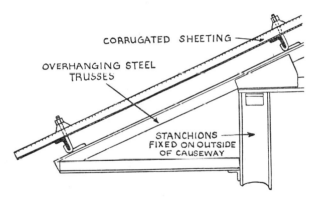

Remember that if the water off the yard roof is run onto an existing roof it will be necessary to enlarge the guttering on that, or it will overflow into the yard.

All covered yards should have gutters with downpipe to a separate drain carrying the rain-water.

Adjustable hay racks and troughs are a great help when the height of the manure is likely to change considerably, but they should be arranged so that they can be filled without entering the yard – and from a trailer if possible.

Fixing troughs on the walls can save quite a lot of time in not having to go into the yard with a tractor and trailer.

Gates can be made adjustable for height quite easily if hung on

191

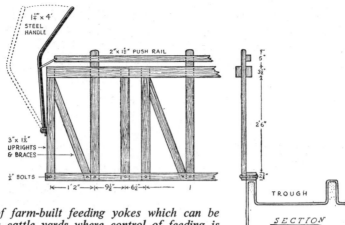

Type of farm-built feeding yokes which can be used in cattle yards where control of feeding is desired.

the stanchions, as it is a simple matter to put sets of hangings at different heights with corresponding catches on the clapping posts.

Feeding yokes as shown in the sketch above save a considerable amount of labour, as the whole row is closed or opened by one movement.

Walls should be of brick or concrete blocks up to a height of about 5'; sheeting can be used above that to save expense.

All floors should be concreted and all waterpipes carried under ground at least 18" deep to prevent risk of frost.

A well-equipped and well-lit farm work-shop, particularly suitable for the larger farm.

These open-fronted loose boxes in course of construction are roofed and partly wall sheeted with one of the new aluminium sheetings now available.

Picture below shows a further use of the same material which is available in various sizes and fitments for principal farm purposes.

Some Examples
of
FARM BUILDING
CONVERSIONS

N

Stable to Milking Parlour

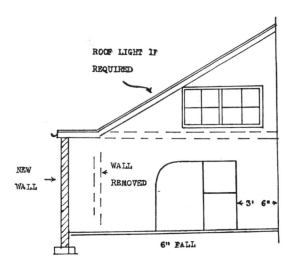

● *Extra width gain-ed by setting steel beam from back wall.*

● *New outside wall built up to take beam weight.*

● *Old wall then re-moved.*

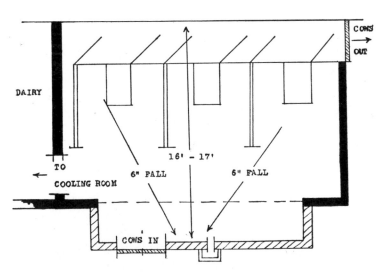

● *Stable 10 ft. floor might have to be removed to satisfy official requirements. All building proposals for milking houses and dairies should be discussed with county milk production officer of A.E.C.*

Stable to Piggery

● *Floor of farrowing bed should be insulated. Kerb will help to keep bedding in place.*

● *Corner railed off for nest should have infra-red lamp above.*

● *Floor to yard needs fairly steep fall.*

● *If there is no loft to stable, false roof is advisable.*

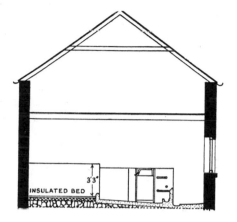

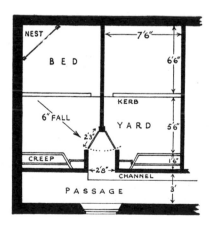

● *Don't let creep depth be less than 1' 6"; otherwise sow may worry pigs in attempting to get their food.*

● *Stall-type piglet self-feeder can be used instead of creep.*

This type of piggery will house sow and large litter up to weaning age – three or four weeks longer if necessary.

195

Loose Box into Calf House

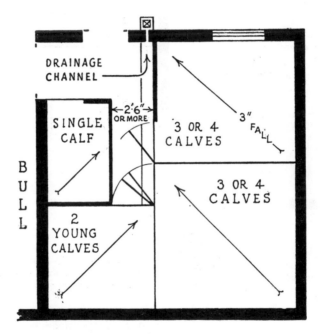

- *Minimum dimensions are: single calf pen 20 sq. ft.; group pens, for older calves, 40 sq. ft. per calf; rack and trough space 2′ per calf.*

- *Solid partition walls are best, they reduce draughts.*

196

Single-Row Cowhouse into Building for Calves or Pigs

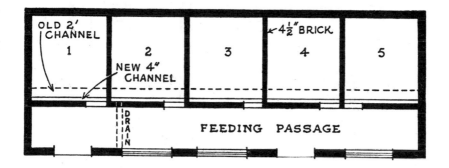

● *Old dung gutter is filled in to leave new channel only 4" wide by 2" deep. Previous exit channel for dung and urine can still be used.*

● *This gives length of approximately 6' 6" to each pen; width can vary according to size of original building and proposed grouping of stock.*

● *Removable troughs will increase adaptability of building – they can be changed according to stock housed.*

Universal Hut
into General-Purpose Pig House

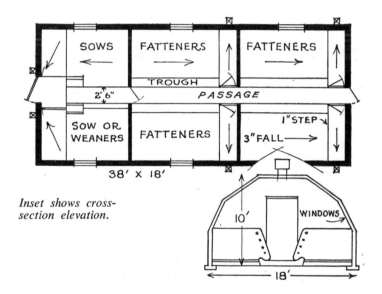

Inset shows cross-section elevation.

● *Use concrete-covered hollow blocks for raised floors, and salt-glazed feeding troughs.*

● *Sides of house are best lined with 3″ concrete blocks up to height of 2′ 6″; if rest of hut can be lined with insulation board, so much the better.*

Nissen Hut
into Farrowing House

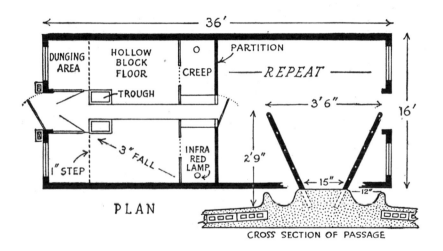

PLAN

CROSS SECTION OF PASSAGE

● *Cross-section of passage (inset) shows height of posts carrying tubular steel rails, and width of walk.*

● *Construction of floor is hollow blocks on concrete with 1¼″–2″ of concrete above.*

199

Stable into
Pig and Poultry House

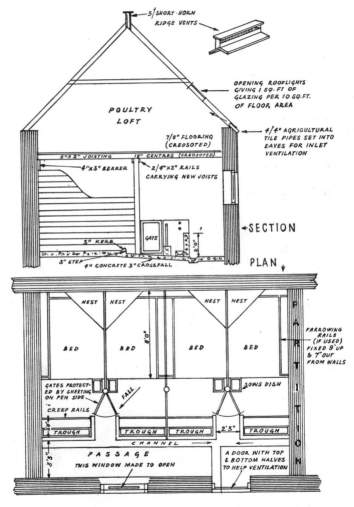

3/SHORT·HORN
RIDGE VENTS

OPENING ROOFLIGHTS
GIVING 1 SQ.FT OF
GLAZING PER 10 SQ.FT.
OF FLOOR AREA

POULTRY
LOFT

7/8" FLOORING
(CREOSOTED)

4/4" AGRICULTURAL
TILE PIPES SET INTO
EAVES FOR INLET
VENTILATION

5"X 2" JOISTING   18" CENTRES (CREOSOTED)

4"X3" BEARER   2/4"X2" RAILS
CARRYING NEW JOISTS

◄SECTION

3" KERB   GATE   2'0"

3" STEP   4" CONCRETE 3"CROSSFALL   PLAN

NEST   NEST   NEST   NEST

8'0"   FARROWING
BED   BED   BED   BED   RAILS
                                                  (IF USED)
                                                  FIXED 9"UP
                                                  & 7"OUT
                                                  FROM WALLS

GATES PROTECT-   SOWS DISH
ED BY SHEETING
ON PEN SIDE
CREEP RAILS   FALL

TROUGH   TROUGH   TROUGH   2'3"   TROUGH

CHANNEL

PASSAGE   A DOOR WITH TOP
THIS WINDOW MADE TO OPEN   & BOTTOM HALVES
                                  TO HELP VENTILATION

PARTITION

● *A building that makes use of both floors – the loft*
for deep-litter poultry, the ground floor for farrowing.

200

Double-Row Cowhouse
into "Black Type" Piggery

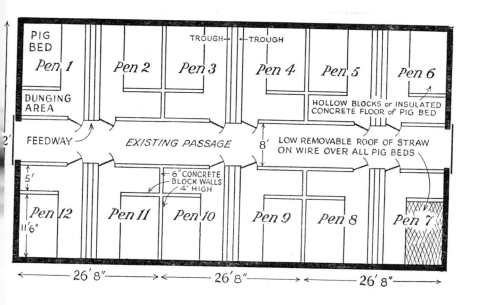

- This makes use of the existing centre passage. Tractor and trailer can travel through for quick mucking out.

- Drainage is best provided by cutting new outlets to side of building rather than relaying floor.

- Note cross-section of construction of feeding way, using iron standards as posts.

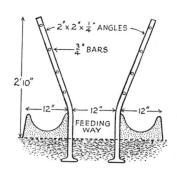

Nissen Hut into Cowhouse

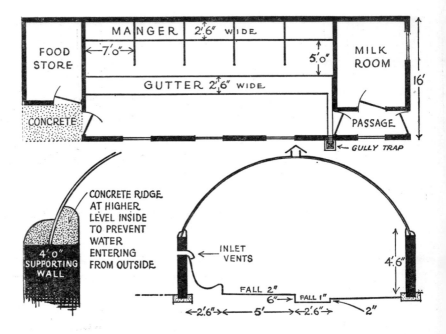

● *Lay gutter first, then falls for remainder of floor can be established. Gutter should fall ½" per cow lengthways.*

● *Milk-room should have about 100 sq. ft. floor area, sloped to drain to outside trapped gulley. Wall behind cooler should be cement rendered.*

● *Windows should be included to give not less than 4 sq. ft. per cow in milking section, one-tenth of floor area in milk-room.*

Fitting New Cowhouse into an Old Yard

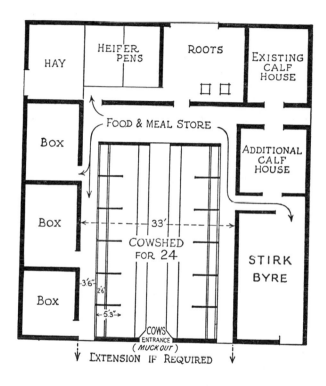

- *Where an old-type yard exists and there is no room for extension, a central cowshed is worth considering.*

- *In this case the idea frees the original small cowshed for division into further calf-house and one for young stock.*

- *Possible snag is that passage round cowshed is too narrow for transport and that ventilation is restricted. In such circumstances, yard and parlour might be better arrangement.*

APPENDIX I

TABLE GIVING FLOOR SPACE AND TROUGH SPACE, ETC., FOR BUILDING TO HOUSE LIVESTOCK:

BULL PENS   150 to 400 sq. ft.

COWS

In yards	90 to 130 sq. ft. per cow
Semi-covered yards	55 to 75 sq. ft. per cow
Waiting yards	15 to 20 sq. ft. per cow
Mangers in yards	2' 6" to 3' (heifers 2')
Calving boxes	120 to 180 sq. ft.

CALF PENS:

One loose box of the above size is suitable for 5 growing calves
Individual pens   12 to 16 sq. ft.

DAIRY:

7 sq. ft. to 14 sq. ft. per cow according to how milk is sold, i.e. farm bottled or in bulk

PIGS:

Fattening pigs	10 to 16 sq. ft. per pig (including dunging passage)
Fattening pigs in yards	30 to 40 sq. ft. per pig
Farrowing pens	60 to 80 sq. ft. per pig
Boar pens	40 to 50 sq. ft. per pig
Troughs:	
Fattening	12 to 15 inches per pig
Sows and litters	30 to 40 inches per pig
Boars	24 to 30 inches per pig
Weaners	9 to 12 inches per pig
Farrowing rails	8 to 10 inches from floor to wall
Dunging passage	Wide enough for tractor and front-mounted fork
Feeding passage	Not less than 4' wide
Divisions	Not less than 4' 6" high

POULTRY:

Intensive housing for hens	4 sq. ft. per bird
Semi-intensive	3 sq. ft. per bird
Slatted floor	1 sq. ft. per bird
Chickens:	
Up to one month intensive	½ sq. ft. per bird
Up to 5 lb. fattened	1 sq. ft. per bird

APPENDIX II

MANURE STORAGE

LIQUID MANURE:
Production per day

Cows 3 gallons
Pigs ⅓ gallon

FARMYARD MANURE:
Production per day

Cows 50 lb.
Pigs 7 lb.

Storage space required – 1 cu. ft. for each 70 lb.

APPENDIX III

TO ESTIMATE CAPACITY OF LIQUID STORAGE TANKS

CIRCULAR

Diameter in feet	Gallons per foot of depth
4	78
6	172
8	314
10	490
12	725
14	960
16	1,256
20	1,960

RECTANGULAR
Six gallons per cubic foot.

APPENDIX IV

STEEL JOISTS AS BEAMS

Safe Distributed Loads in Tons for Spans in Feet

Based on B.S.449. Revised 1948

Size in inches	3	4	5	6	7	8	10	12	14	16
3×1½	2·4	1·8	—	—	—	—	—	—	—	—
3×3	5·6	4·2	—	—	—	—	—	—	—	—
4×1¾	4·0	3·0	2·4	2·0	—	—	—	—	—	—
4×3	8·35	6·26	5·01	4·17	—	—	—	—	—	—
4×3	8·6	6·4	5·1	4·3	—	—	—	—	—	—
4¾×1⅞	6·2	4·7	3·7	3·1	2·6	—	—	—	—	—
5×2⅛	9·55	7·16	5·73	4·77	4·09	3·58	—	—	—	—
5×3	12·1	9·1	7·2	6·0	5·2	4·5	—	—	—	—
5×4½	—	15·13	12·1	10·09	8·64	7·56	—	—	—	—
6×3	15·5	11·6	9·3	7·7	6·6	5·8	—	—	—	—
6×4½	25·7	19·2	15·4	12·8	11·0	9·6	—	—	—	—
6×5	—	24·2	19·4	16·1	13·8	12·1	—	—	—	—
7×3½	—	17·0	13·6	11·33	9·71	8·5	6·8	—	—	—
7×4	—	18·8	15·0	12·5	10·7	9·4	7·5	—	—	—
8×4	—	23·1	18·5	15·4	13·2	11·5	9·2	7·7	—	—
8×5	—	—	29·8	24·9	21·3	18·6	14·9	12·4	—	—
8×6	—	—	—	31·9	27·3	23·9	19·1	15·9	—	—
9×4	—	30·0	24·0	20·0	17·1	15·0	12·0	10·0	8·5	—
9×7	—	—	—	—	—	38·5	30·8	25·6	22·0	—
9×7	—	—	—	—	—	42·54	34·03	28·36	24·3	—
10×4½	—	—	32·6	27·1	23·3	20·3	16·3	13·5	11·6	10·1
10×5	—	—	39·0	32·5	27·8	24·3	19·5	16·2	13·9	12·1
10×6	—	—	—	—	39·0	34·1	27·3	22·7	19·5	17·0

APPENDIX V

USEFUL ADDRESSES FOR REFERENCE:

INCORPORATED ASSOCIATION OF ARCHITECTS AND
SURVEYORS, 75 Eaton Place, London, S.W.1

LANDS IMPROVEMENT COMPANY,
58 Victoria Street, Westminster, London, S.W.1.

THE AGRICULTURAL MORTGAGE CORPORATION LTD,
Stone House, Bishopsgate, London, E.C.2

THE ROYAL INSTITUTE OF CHARTERED SURVEYORS,
12 Great George Street, Westminster, London, S.W.1

THE INCORPORATED ASSOCIATION OF ARCHITECTS AND
SURVEYORS, 75 Eaton Place, London, S.W.1

CEMENT AND CONCRETE ASSOCIATION
52 Grosvenor Gardens, London, S.W.1

TIMBER DEVELOPMENT ASSOCIATION,
21 College Hill, London, E.C.4

RURAL INDUSTRIES BUREAU
35 Camp Road, Wimbledon, London, S.W.17

INDEX

A

Adaptation of buildings, 22
Agricultural Land Service, 25
Aluminium sheeting, for roofing, 92
—, for walls, 82–83
—, method of fixing on roofs, 92–93
Anchor bolts, 61–62
Angle tiles for roofs, 96

Architect's plans, 28–29
Asbestos cement sheeting, cutting, 93
—, fixing on roofs, 92
—, for roofs, 31, 90–91
—, for walls, 82–83
—, weights and sizes, 91

B

Ball valves, 111–112
Beams, safe loads for, 208
Bib-cocks, 111
Bitumen for damp courses, 75–76
— painting, 162
Blocks, concrete, 33, 34–35
—, —, kinds of, 35
—, —, numbers required, 35
—, —, size of, 35
—, interlocking, 33, 35
Board and felt, method of roofing, 97
Bonding, 72–73
Borrowing money for farm buildings, 18

Bricklaying, 72–77
—, tools required, 73
—, method of working, 74–77
Bricks, 33
—, buying, 33
—, number required, 33
—, size of, 33
Building materials required, 107
Buildings, some examples of conversions, 193–203
Building walls in concrete, 33
Bushes, removing, 41

C

Cable for farm electric wiring, 170, 171
Capped tiles for roofs, 96
Cattle grids, 181–183
Cavity walls, 77
Cement, buying and storing, 36
—, if damp, 36
—, rapid-hardening, 36
—, varieties, 36
—, washes, 164–165
Centre-nailing for slates, 96

Collar roof, 90
Concrete blocks, 33, 34–35
—, kinds of, 35
—, laying, 77–78
—, numbers required, 35
Concrete curing, 148–149
Concrete floors, insulation, 149–150
Concrete frames, 31
—, erection, 67–70
—, parts of, 70
Concrete mixers, 64–65

211

C—*cont.*

D

E

F

F—*cont.*

G

H

I

L

M

N

P

R

S